CEB/FIP Manual on

BENDING
AND COMPRESSION

DESIGN OF SECTIONS UNDER AXIAL ACTION EFFECTS AT THE ULTIMATE LIMIT STATE

Prepared by

Comité Euro-International du Béton (CEB)
Euro-International Committee for Concrete

in co-operation with

Fédération Internationale de la Précontrainte (FIP)
International organisation for the development of concrete, prestressing
and related materials and techniques

Editorial team

E Grasser,	*München, W Germany* (Chairman)
A G Meseguer,	*Madrid, Spain*
P J Montoya,	*Madrid, Spain*
W Moosecker,	*München, W Germany*
F Morán	*Madrid, Spain*
J Perchat,	*Paris, France*
G Thielen,	*Paris, France*

Construction Press
London and New York

Although the Comité Euro-International du Béton and the Fédération Internationale de la Précontrainte do their best to ensure that any information they may give is accurate, no liability or responsibility of any kind (including liability for negligence) is accepted in this respect by the Comité and/or the Fédération, their members, their servants or agents.

Construction Press
Longman House
Burnt Mill, Harlow, Essex, UK

A division of Longman Group Ltd, London.

*Published in the United States of America by
Longman Inc, New York.*

© Comité Euro-International du Béton (CEB) 1982

First published 1982

British Library Cataloguing in Publication Data

CEB/FIP manual on bending and compression.
  1. Prestressed concrete – Design and construction
  I. Comité Euro-International du Béton
  II. Fédération Internationale de la
Précontrainte
  624.1'834   TA683.9

  ISBN 0-86095-701-2

Library of Congress Cataloging in Publication Data
Main entry under title:

CEB/FIP manual on bending and compression.

  "The final draft of this design manual was presented as CEB-Bulletin 135 to and approved for publication by the 21. plenary session of the CEB in Budapest in May 1980" – Foreword.
  Bibliography: p.
  Includes index.
  1. Reinforced concrete construction – Handbooks, manuals, etc. 2. Structural design – Handbooks, manuals, etc. 3. Strains and stresses – Handbooks, manuals, etc. I. Grasser, Emil, Dipl.-Ing. II. Comité euro-international du béton. III. Fédération internationale de la précontrainte. IV. Title: Bending and compression.

TA683.22.C38   624.1'8341   81-19438
ISBN 0-86095-701-2   AACR2

Typeset on IBM by Lonsdale Typesetting Services
and printed in Great Britain by Pitman Press Ltd, Bath

BENDING
AND COMPRESSION

HUBERT RÜSCH
in memoriam
1903—1979

Some of his numerous merits which will make his name unforgettable have been his fundamental studies of the behaviour of concrete and his researches towards the modern flexural theory of reinforced concrete. The origin and the shape of this manual owe substantial impulses to him.

Foreword

The final draft of this Design Manual was presented as CEB-Bulletin 135 to, and approved for publication by, the 21st Plenary Session of CEB in Budapest in May 1980. In accordance with the intentions of the CEB it contains:

a) in the following a short description of its scope;
b) the wording of the relevant clauses of the Model Code (§10);
c) some general comments on safety considerations, the determination of design action-effects and the basic assumptions for the design of sections under axial action-effects;
d) proposals for appropriate design procedures (formulae, diagrams, tables) for a variety of design problems for reinforced and prestressed sections;
e) numerical examples for each design procedure.

The scope of this manual was determined by the following considerations:

— Only the design of sections at the ultimate limit state for axial stress states is treated. In Appendix 3, the limitation of the concrete compressive stresses at the serviceability limit state is briefly dealt with.

— In Chapter 2, general safety requirements and basic design principles are pointed out and are briefly commented to avoid misunderstandings. Answers on questions concerning the reasons and derivations (why-questions) are not given in this manual.

— The determination of design action-effects (influence of non-linearities, determination of worst combinations) are not treated in the manual. Information regarding these questions can be obtained from the Notes of the Model Code (left column), from the CEB-Complements and from other literature.

— The design procedures presented aim at producing the minimum total amount of reinforcement for a given cross-section and action-effects. In practical design, other reinforcement arrangements may be optimal with respect to economic considerations or be dictated by minimum reinforcement requirements (§18.1.1.1 of the Model Code).

— The design aids are provided for the reinforcement grades S220, S400 and S500 which are most commonly used and defined in Euronorm 80. Design aids are provided for rectangular, T-sections, circular and annular cross-sections with different relative concrete cover. For rectangular sections in skew bending, diagrams are given for different reinforcement arrangements. With these aids, most of the design problems usually encountered in practice can be solved. Thus, this manual is no more only a Model Manual for national design manuals, as it was meant to be in the past.

— To reduce the size of the manual, design aids are only provided for the idealized bilinear stress—strain diagram for the reinforcing steel. They are, however, also approximately valid for steel cold worked by axial torsion and/or tension for which the Model Code gives a more accurate stress—strain relationship.

— Design aids are only prepared for common types of cross-sections. For unusual sections, it is recommended to use the rectangular instead of the parabolic—rectangular distribution of concrete stresses in the compression zone for design. The application is explained with formulae and an example.

— With respect to prestressed concrete, it is only shown in which way a prestressing force should be taken into account for the design at the ultimate limit state. A numerical example is also included.

— The manual is supplemented by three appendixes:

App. 1: contains information on the determination of the effective width of T-beams.

App. 2: contains design aids for plane structural elements (plates, slabs) with reinforcement direction deviating from the direction of principal stresses. Formulae are given for elements with orthogonal and skew reinforcement.

App. 3: contains considerations and aids for the limitation of concrete stresses at the serviceability limit state.

— The bibliography is limited to CEB-documents which contain the basis and derivation of the CEB bending theory and which show the development of the manual.

— An index table of the design aids is provided on page xi which can be helpful to find the appropriate aid easily.

The Editorial Group for this manual consisted of:

E Grasser, München, Chairman
A G Meseguer, Madrid
P J Montoya, Madrid
W Moosecker, München
F Morán, Madrid
J Perchat, Paris
G Thielen, Paris

H Rüsch† (München), F Levi (Torino), S Schröder (Dresden), Th Baumann (München), A W Beeby (Wexham Springs), D Linse (München) and G Mancini (Torino) have assisted us with valuable contributions and recommendations. All of those who have helped producing this manual deserve our thanks.

E Grasser

München,
April 1981

Contents

Index of Design Aids (Tables and Charts)

Cross-section	Range of Application	Characteristics of Design Aid		Design Aid No. S 220	S 400	S 500
	Prevailing bending in the plane of symmetry	General Diagram		1		
		General Table	$A_{s2} = 0$	2		
			$A_{s2} \neq 0$	3	4	5
		General Table	$h_f/d \leq 0{,}15$	6		
			$h_f/d \geq 0{,}20$	7		
	Prevailing compression in the plane of symmetry	Interaction Diagram $A_{s1} = A_{s2}$	$d_1/h = 0{,}05$	8	13 14*	21 22*
			$d_1/h = 0{,}10$	9	15 16*	23 24*
			$d_1/h = 0{,}15$	10	17 18*	25 26*
			$d_1/h = 0{,}20$	11	19	27
			$d_1/h = 0{,}25$	12	20	28
		Interaction Diagram	$d_1/h = 0{,}10$	29	32	35
			$r_i/r = 0{,}70$	30	33	36
$d_1/(r-r_i) = 0{,}50$			$r_i/r = 0{,}90$	31	34	37
	Biaxial bending with and without compression	Interaction Diagram $d_1/h = b_1/b = 0{,}10$		38	42 43*	50
				39	44 45*	51
				40	46 47*	52
				41	48 49*	53

*) Enlargement of inner part

Notations

In the following, only the frequently used notations are listed. Symbols which are rarely used are explained at the places where they appear.

Main letters

A = area of cross-section
E = modulus of elasticity
F = force
I = moment of inertia
M = bending moment
N = normal force
P = prestressing force
R = resistance
S = action-effect

d = effective height
e = eccentricity
f = strength of a material
h = overall height
r = radius
x = height of compression zone
y = distance between axis of reinforcement and neutral axis
z = lever arm of internal forces

γ = partial safety factor
ϵ = strain
ζ = z/d reduced lever arm of internal forces
μ = reduced bending moment
ν = reduced normal force
ξ = x/d reduced height of compression zone
σ = stress
ψ = load combination factor
ω = mechanical percentage of reinforcement

Subscripts

R = resistance
S = action-effect

c = concrete
d = design value
f = flange (e.g., flange height h_f), action (e.g., partial safety factor for action γ_f)
g = permanent action
k = characteristic value
m = mean (e.g., mean value of prestressing force P_m), material (e.g., partial safety factor for material strength γ_m)
p = prestressing steel (A_p), with respect to the axis of prestressing steel (M_p)
q = variable action
s = reinforcing steel (A_s), with respect to the axis of reinforcing steel (M_s)
t = time
w = web
y = at yielding (f_y)

x
y $\Big\}$ = coordinate directions
z

1 = tension zone or less compressed face
2 = compression zone or more compressed face
ef = effective
lim = limit
tot = total

1. Ultimate limit states of resistance to axial load effects

1.1 CLAUSES OF THE CEB/FIP MODEL CODE ON THE RESISTANCE TO AXIAL LOAD EFFECTS (§10)

The safety domain is bounded by a curve (or a surface in the case of skew bending) representing the interaction between moment and internal axial force.

For scalar load-effects, equation [6.8] is directly applicable, for example:

- in simple tension: $\qquad N_{Sd} \leqslant N_{Rd}$ $\qquad$ [10.1]
- in simple bending: $\qquad M_{Sd} \leqslant M_{Rd}$ $\qquad$ [10.2]

Provided that it does not reach 15°, the deviation can be considered to be neglibible. For greater deviations see the CEB/FIP Bending Compression Manual.*

10.1 GENERAL

For the applied design load effects, refer to Clauses 6.1 and 6.4.2.2.1.

For each applied load effect, the extreme resultant vector which defines that load effect must be within a limit domain of which the boundary corresponds to the ultimate resistant load effects determined by the rules in this section.

10.2 SCOPE

This section is applicable only to linear elements, as defined in 7.2.1.1 and to slabs in which the deviation of the centre line of the reinforcement from the principal directions of the axial stresses is negligible.

10.3 SECTIONS

For top slabs subjected to tension, Clause 8.6 applies, in addition to the following:

In the zone over the supports of continuous beams the only tension reinforcement to be considered in the design calculations for the resistant load effects shall be that which is contained within a slab width not exceeding the width of the support plus one-fifth of the distance between the points of zero moment on either side of the support under consideration.

10.4 BONDED REINFORCEMENT

10.4.1 Basis of design

10.4.1.1 *Assumptions*

The calculation of the resistant load effects is based on the following assumptions, additional to those given in 10.4.2, 10.4.3 and 10.4.4:

a) plane sections remain plane;
b) the reinforcement is subjected to the same variations in strain as the adjacent concrete;
c) the tensile strength of the concrete is neglected;
d) the maximum compressive strain of the concrete is taken to be:
 - 0.0035 in bending (simple or compound, straight or skew)
 - 0.002 in axial compression.

*See Appendix 2 of this manual.

This limitation is a conventional one which applies to the verification of the individual sections (local checking). Where the tensile reinforcement is close together the value of 0.01 can be taken at the position of its centre of gravity.

A sensibly equivalent procedure consists of using increased values of the coefficients γ_c and γ_s for the calculation of the resistant load effects, by multiplying them with

$$\gamma_n = \frac{b + 60}{b} \nleq 1.1 \qquad [10.4]$$

where b denotes the smallest dimension of the cross-section, expressed in mm.

This resistant load effect is then compared with the applied load effect determined without taking account of the minimum eccentricity.

Taking all moments from the centroid of the tension reinforcement and denoting by

— M_{Sd} the applied design moment

— M_{Rd1}, M_{Rd2} the design resistant moments

corresponding to positions AB and BC of the strain diagram respectively, the diagram corresponding to M_{Sd} will be assumed to pass:

— through A   if $M_{Sd} \leqslant M_{Rd1}$ [10.5]

— through B   if $M_{Rd1} \leqslant M_{Sd} \leqslant M_{Rd2}$ [10.6]

— through C   if $M_{Sd} \geqslant M_{Rd2}$ [10.7]

A strain diagram passing through A corresponds:

— either to simple tension (vertical line from A) or tension with a slight eccentricity (neutral axis outside the section)

— or to simple or compound bending within the strength capacity of the concrete.

A strain diagram passing through B corresponds to simple or compound bending, the strength of the concrete being exceeded (neutral axis outside the section).

A strain diagram passing through C corresponds either to compound bending, the section being entirely in compression (neutral axis outside the section) or to simple compression (vertical line through C).

The use of other idealised diagrams can be accepted, provided that the results obtained in this way agree satisfactorily with those given by the parabola—rectangle diagram or always remain on the safe side.

The coefficient 0.85 takes account of the reduction in compressive strength depending on the mode of application of the load, for example of the unfavourable effect of a sustained load, but it does not fulfil the function of a safety coefficient.

It should be noted that the diagram in Fig. 10.2 cannot be used for the determination of the longitudinal modulus of deformation, nor in general for a non-linear analysis according to Clause 8.4.

e) the maximum tensile strain in the reinforcement is taken to be 0.01.

f) the total deformation of all the prestressing tendons is calculated by taking into account the preliminary elongation corresponding to the representative value of the prestressing force taken into account for the calculations; the variation in the elongation beyond the preliminary elongation ϵ_{pt} is limited to 0.01.

10.4.1.2 *Element under centric compression or with a small eccentricity*

To take account of the uncertainty of the point of application of the external force, the applied design load effect is determined by successively introducing a minimum eccentricity along both principal axes of the sections:

$$e_{min} \geqslant h/30 \text{ and } b/30 \text{ successively,}$$
$$\text{and } 20 \text{ mm,} \qquad [10.3]$$

where h and b are the dimensions measured along these axes.

10.4.2 Strain distribution

Assumptions a, d and e in 10.4.1.1 are supplemented as follows:

for calculating the resisting load-effect, it is assumed that the strain diagram must pass through one of the three points A, B or C defined in Fig. 10.1.

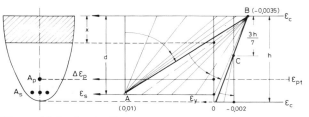

Figure 10.1   Strain diagram

10.4.3   Idealised stress—strain diagrams for the concrete

10.4.3.1 *Parabola—rectangle diagram*

For calculating the resistant load effects, an idealised diagram is used for the concrete, such as that given in Fig. 10.2.

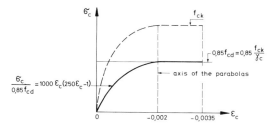

Figure 10.2   Parable—rectangle diagram

The case envisaged relates to a strain diagram passing through A or B (Fig. 10.1). If the strain diagram passes through point C, the rectangular diagram can still be used, provided that the ultimate compressive strain in the concrete at the most highly stressed compression fibre does not differ greatly from -0.0035.

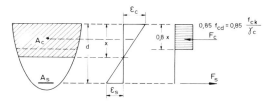

Figure 10.3   Rectangular diagram

The value 0.80 f_{cd} should be adopted, for example, for zones of circular or triangular shape with a taper on the compression side or trapezoidal (encountered in rectangular sections subjected to skew bending).

For example, for the simplified diagram in Fig. 3.1.

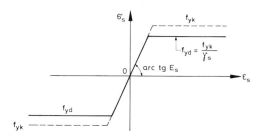

Figure 10.4   Design diagram for the reinforcement

As a consequence of the lack of bond, slip can take place between the tendons and the concrete, resulting in a reduction in the maximum stress attained by these tendons, and in a considerable reduction of the load-carrying capacity of the structural element.

See FIP document [17].

10.4.3.2   *Rectangular diagram*

If the section is not entirely in compression, a simplified rectangular distribution of the compressive stresses can be permitted; that distribution is defined as follows (where x is the depth to the neutral axis of the section):

1) for a distance of 0.2 x from the neutral axis, the stress is zero,

2) for the remaining distance 0.8 x, the stress is constant and has a value of:
   - 0.85 f_{cd} for compression zones of constant width or for those in which the width increases towards the extreme fibre in compression.

   - 0.80 f_{cd} for compression zones the width of which decreases towards these same fibres.

10.4.4   Design stress—strain diagrams for the steel

The design diagram for ordinary reinforcing steel or for the steel used in prestressing tendons is deduced from the characteristic diagram by drawing a line parallel to the tangent at the origin, in the proportion $1/\gamma_s$.

10.5   UNBONDED TENDONS

For the ultimate strength limit state under axial action effects, in the case of a section containing unbonded prestressing tendons special verification is required.

2. General safety requirements and basic design principles

2.1 GENERAL SAFETY REQUIREMENTS

The aim of design is the achievement of acceptable probabilities that the structure being designed will not become unfit for the use for which it is required during its intended life. A structure, or part of a structure, is considered to have become unfit for its intended purpose when it reaches a limit state in which one of the criteria relating to its load-bearing capacity or its conditions of service is infringed.

The limit states are placed into two categories:

a) the ultimate limit states, which correspond to the maximum load-bearing capacity;

b) the serviceability limit states, which are related to the criteria governing normal use and durability.

In the following, only the verification of adequate safety at the ultimate limit state is considered. In the majority of cases, this can be ensured by checking that in all sections the calculated design action-effects S_d do not exceed the corresponding design resistances R_d.

$$S_d \leqslant R_d \qquad (2.1)$$

2.2 DETERMINATION OF THE DESIGN ACTION-EFFECTS

The determination of load effects is treated in §7 and §9 of the Model Code. The following types of structural analysis are allowed:

— linear analysis,
— linear analysis with moment redistribution,
— non-linear analysis,
— plastic analysis.

The choice of the type of analysis to be adopted is influenced by various considerations, such as possible causes of non-linearity, the practicability of the calculations and the cost of the analysis compared to the cost of the structure itself. Even when significant causes of non-linearity exist, a linear analysis may frequently be used.

If condition (2.1) is checked for different sections, the design values of the action-effects S_d must be determined from the characteristic values of the actions from

$$S_d = S \left\{ \gamma_g G + \gamma_p P + \gamma_q \left[Q_{1k} + \sum_{i>1} (\psi_{oi} Q_{ik}) \right] \right\} \qquad (2.2)$$

or in the case of a linear analysis from

$$S_d = \gamma_g S_g + \gamma_p S_p + \gamma_q \left[S_{q1k} + \sum_{i>1} (\psi_{oi} S_{qik}) \right] \qquad (2.3)$$

In these formulae are:

$\gamma_g, \gamma_p, \gamma_q$ partial safety coefficients (see Table 2.1)

G representative value of the permanent section

P representative value of the prestressing force

Table 2.1 Partial safety factors γ_f for actions

Actions	γ_f	Unfavourable effect	Favourable effect
Permanent	γ_g	1.35	1.0
Prestress	γ_p	1.2	0.9
Variable	γ_q	1.5	Not to be taken into account

Q_{1k} characteristic value of the variable action taken as basic action (if it is not evident which variable action must be taken as basic action, each variable action must be taken as basic action to determine the most unfavourable load effect)

Q_{ik} other variable actions

ψ_{0i} combination factors

$S_g, S_p, \ldots$ load effects due to G, P, . . .

In this manual, it is assumed that the most unfavourable design load effects S_d have been determined in accordance with the Model Code.

2.3 DESIGN RESISTANCE TO AXIAL LOAD EFFECTS

2.3.1 Basic assumptions

Axial load effects are considered to be those which cause only normal stresses in a cross-section.

§10 of the Model Code applies to linear elements and to slabs in which the direction of the reinforcement does not deviate from the direction of principal stresses by more than $15°$. The design of plane elements with a deviation exceeding this value is treated in Appendix 2 of this manual.

The calculation of the resistance to axial load effects is based on the following assumptions (more information about the theoretical background will be found in the Complements to the Model Code):

a) Plane sections remain plane.
Deformations due to shear forces are neglected.

b) The reinforcement is subjected to the same variations in strain as the adjacent concrete.
It is assumed that there is no slip between concrete and steel.

c) The tensile strength of concrete is neglected.
The tensile strength can in many cases be absorbed by shrinkage or temperature-induced stresses not considered in design.

d) A definition of the possible strain diagrams at the ultimate limit state (this is discussed in more detail in 2.3.2).

e) Design stress-strain diagrams for concrete and steel (these are discussed in 2.3.3 and 2.3.4).

f) The total deformation of all the prestressing tendons is calculated by taking into account the preliminary elongation corresponding to the representative value of the prestressing force taken into account for the calculations.

The resisting load effects are determined as a function of the design stress-strain diagrams. These are derived from characteristic stress-strain relationships by means of partial safety coefficients γ_m (see Table 2.2). For the values $\gamma_c = 1.5$ and $\gamma_s = 1.15$ a normal standard of quality control in accordance with §23 of the Model Code is assumed. If that standard cannot be reached or is exceeded, other values for γ_c and γ_s can be considered.

Table 2.2 Partial safety factors γ_m for materials

Combination	Concrete γ_c	Steel γ_s
Basic	1.5	1.15
Accidental	1.3	1.0

2.3.2 Strain distributions at the ultimate limit state

The failure of a reinforced or prestressed cross-section under axial action-effects is caused by the rupture of concrete in the compression zone. For sections with low percentages of reinforcement, this rupture is initiated by excessive plastic deformations of the yielding reinforcement.

According to the Model Code, it is assumed that the strain diagram at the ultimate limit state must pass through one of the points A, B or C defined in Fig. 2.1. Considering the limiting values of concrete and steel strain, five zones of the possible strain profiles can be distinguished.

Figure 2.1   Strain diagrams at the ultimate limit state

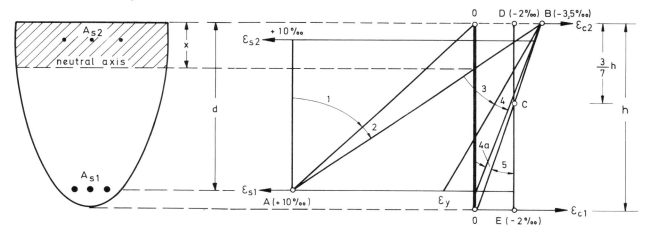

Zones 1 and 2

These zones are both characterized by the reinforcement closest to the tension face of the section being at the limiting strain of 10‰. The strain profiles at the ultimate limit state for all sections in these zones pass through point A in Fig. 2.1.

Zone 1: The entire section is in tension, the neutral axis lies outside the section.

Zone 2: The neutral axis lies within the section, there is thus both a compression and a tension zone. The maximum strain in the concrete is less than the limiting value of $-3.5‰$, thus the strength of the concrete is not exhausted. The boundary between zones 2 and 3 is defined by a strain diagram where both the maximum concrete strain ($\epsilon_c = -3.5‰$) and reinforcement strain ($\epsilon_s = 10‰$) are present.

Zones 3 and 4

These zones are characterized by the ultimate compressive strain in the concrete reaching $-3.5‰$; all strain profiles for sections pass through point B in Fig. 2.1.

Zone 3: The strain in the steel at failure lies between 10‰ and ϵ_y, the strain corresponding to the design strength of the steel f_{yd}. The boundary between zones 3 and 4 is called the balanced condition.

Zone 4: The strain in the steel at failure lies between ϵ_y and zero. The steel stress at the ultimate limit state is thus less than f_{yd}.

Zone 4a: All the steel is in compression. Some small part of the section remains in tension.

Zone 5

The entire section is in compression. All strain profiles pass through point C inside the section (see Fig. 2.1.). The maximal compressive strain of concrete is between $-2‰$ and $-3.5‰$. The point C is the point where the line BO (which defines the boundary between sections partially in tension and sections in compression only) intersects the line DE (defining the conditions in a section subjected to pure compression). The distance of this point from the outermost compressive fibre is equal to 3/7 of the total depth h of the section.

7

2.3.3 Stress distribution for concrete (stress–strain curves)

Concrete compressive strength is determined by testing specimens cast from the same concrete as that used for the structure. The characteristic strength f_{ck} is defined as that strength below which 5% of all possible strength measurements at the age of 28 days may be expected to fall.

The design strength f_{cd} of concrete is obtained by dividing the characteristic strength f_{ck} by the partial safety factor γ_c. This reduction is meant to account for:

— random variations of the concrete production process,
— deviations of in-situ concrete strength from test specimen strength,
— random variations of concrete strength due to placing, vibrating and curing of concrete.

To obtain the maximum permissible concrete stress, the design concrete strength is further multiplied by a factor of 0.85 to account for the possible strength reduction due to unfavourable modes of load application, mainly sustained loading. This factor does not have the function of a safety factor.

The behaviour of the concrete under concentric and eccentric compression which can be represented by stress–strain relationships depends on various parameters. The most important of these are:

— strength of concrete
— age of concrete at the time of commencement of loading
— rate, duration and repetition of loading
— strain gradient across the section
— shape of cross-sections.

The parameters mentioned above have been studied experimentally and theoretically in order to find an approximation for the stress distribution in concrete at the ultimate limit state which is as far as possible in accordance with the compatibility conditions which are governed by the experimentally measured strain-gradients. CEB-Bulletin No. 36 [3] reports in detail on these investigations. As a result, the parabolic–rectangular approximation of the concrete stress distribution at the ultimate limit state has been developed.

This parabolic–rectangular curve is formed by a second degree parabola extended by a straight line. The apex of the parabola corresponds to a strain of $-2‰$ and the extreme corner of the rectangle corresponds to a strain of $-3‰$ (see Fig. 2.2).

Figure 2.2 Parabolic–rectangular stress–strain distribution for concrete

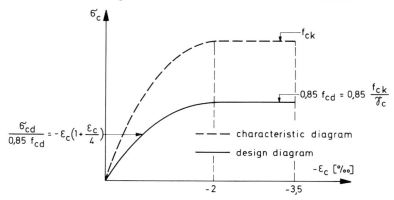

The maximum ordinate of the design diagram corresponds to a stress equal to $0.85\,f_{cd}$ $= 0.85\,f_{ck}/\gamma_c$. The design stress–strain distribution is obtained from the stresses of the characteristic distribution using a partial safety factor γ_c

$$\sigma_{cd} = 0.85\,\frac{\sigma_{ck}}{\gamma_c} \tag{2.4}$$

If the section is not entirely in compression, a simplified rectangular stress–strain diagram for concrete compressive stresses may be used. This is defined as follows (see Fig. 2.3):

a) for a distance of 0.2 x from the neutral axis, the stress is zero,

Figure 2.3   Rectangular stress–strain distribution for concrete

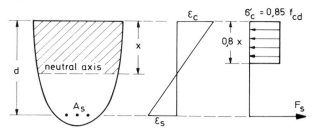

b) for the remaining distance 0.8 x, the stress is constant and has a value of:
  – 0.85 f_{cd} for compression zones of constant width or increasing width towards the extreme fibre in compression,
  – 0.80 f_{cd} for compression zones of decreasing width towards this fibre.

The rectangular distribution of concrete stress has been chosen such that the calculated steel areas obtained using it will be approximately the same as those obtained from use of the parabolic–rectangular diagram. Close agreement with the parabolic–rectangular curve is obtained for zones 2, 3 and 4 (see 2.3.2 of this manual).

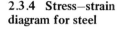

2.3.4 Stress–strain diagram for steel

The characteristic stress–strain curve to be adopted should in general be obtained from the actual stress–strain relationship of the particular steel being used.

For normal reinforcing steel, the actual stress–strain relationship can be replaced by bilinear or trilinear simplifications provided that the approximations are on the safe side. In the absence of more accurate information, the bilinear diagram shown in Fig. 2.4 can be used for mild steel or for steel cold worked by drawing or rolling. For steel cold worked by axial torsion and/or tension, an idealized diagram is given in §3.1.6.1 of the Model Code.

For prestressing steel, the bilinear simplification shown in Fig. 2.4 is generally too crude.

Figure 2.4   Stress–strain distribution for mild steel or steel cold worked by drawing or rolling

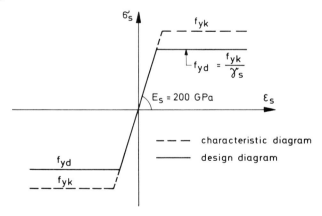

The points of the design stress–strain curve are defined as the points on parallels to the tangent at the origin through the points of the characteristic diagram such that

$$\sigma_{sd} = \frac{\sigma_{sk}}{\gamma_s} \qquad (2.5)$$

This regulation reflects the fact that the modulus of elasticity for steel (E_s = 200 GPa) has only a very small dispersion. For the simplified bilinear stress–strain diagram the design curve is shown in Fig. 2.4.

The design aids given in Chapter 3 are based on the bilinear simplifications of the stress–strain relationship for steel.

2.4 INTERACTION BETWEEN MOMENTS AND NORMAL FORCE

Any axial action-effect can be represented by a vector consisting of a normal force N acting at the centroid of the section and two moments M_y and M_z acting in the direction of the y- and z-coordinates.

For sections with given dimensions and reinforcement, all the possible combinations of N_d, M_{yd} and M_{zd} at the ultimate limit state form an "interaction surface" in a space with N-, M_y-, M_z-coordinates which are in many cases substituted by non-dimensional ν-, μ_y-, μ_z-coordinates. A section is designed properly if the point given by the vector of acting action-effects lies inside or on the interaction surface.

In the common case where one of the bending moments is zero, the interaction surfaces reduce to interaction diagrams (see Fig. 2.5).

Figure 2.5 Idealized interaction diagram for combined axial loading and bending moment

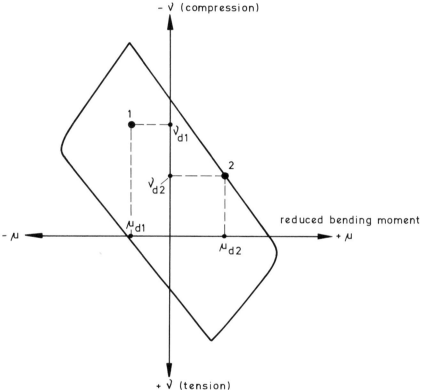

In the design process, two problems can be distinguished.

a) Checking the safety. It is checked whether the point corresponding to the acting design load effects lies inside the region bounded by the interaction surface for the section and reinforcement chosen beforehand (point 1 in Fig. 2.5).

b) Dimensioning of the section. The required amount of reinforcement is determined such that the point corresponding to the acting design load effects lies on the interaction surface (point 2 in Fig. 2.5).

3. Design procedures

3.1 GENERAL COMMENT

In the following, design procedures are described and design aids are given for the design of sections under axial action-effects at the ultimate limit state. Action-effects are considered if they cause only axial stresses in a cross-section (bending moments, axial forces).

The action-effects are often reduced to a non-dimensional form:

$$\nu = \frac{N}{bhf_{cd}} \tag{3.1}$$

$$\mu = \frac{M}{bd^2 \cdot f_{cd}} \quad \text{in the case of prevailing bending} \tag{3.2a}$$

$$\mu = \frac{M}{bh^2 \cdot f_{cd}} \quad \text{in the case of prevailing compression} \tag{3.2b}$$

with:

- μ = reduced bending moment
- M = bending moment
- ν = reduced axial force
- N = axial force
- b = section width
- d = distance between centroid of reinforcement and concrete fibre with minimum strain
- h = total depth of cross-section
- f_{cd} = design strength of concrete.

It is assumed that the designer has already determined the most unfavourable combination of action-effects at the design level. It must be noted that design aids which are only applicable for a specified grade of reinforcing steel are derived for basic combination of actions. Safe approximate results can be obtained with these design aids if the partial safety coefficient γ_s for steel is smaller than 1.15 as for accidental combinations of actions.

The design procedures do not take serviceability requirements, such as control of cracking, into account, nor do they include any consideration of minimum area of longitudinal reinforcement as specified in §18.1.1.1 of the Model Code.

The design aids are based on the bilinear stress–strain relationship for steel (Fig. 2.4) and the parabolic–rectangle stress–strain relationship for the concrete (Fig. 2.2).

In general, a design procedure should aim to provide, for given action-effects, the geometrical and mechanical member properties (concrete cross-section, area and location of reinforcement, strengths of concrete and reinforcement) which are optimal from the structural and economical point of view. In practice, the dimensions of the cross-section and the material properties are commonly already fixed and the design procedure is merely used to find the required areas of reinforcement. In this manual it is assumed that the optimal reinforcement arrangement is one which leads to a minimum area of steel for given action-effects.

Figure 3.1 Optimal reinforcement arrangements for combined axial load and bending moment

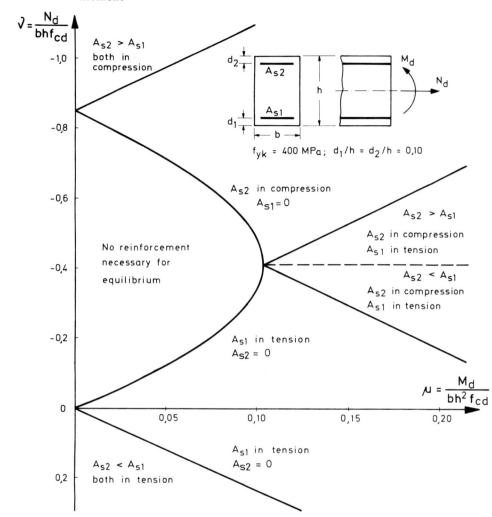

By means of an interaction diagram, Fig. 3.1 shows, for a rectangular cross-section, the different zones of reinforcement distributions which correspond to minimum areas of steel from the theoretical point of view. More detailed information can be found in CEB Bulletin No. 83 [7].

For practical application, design procedures should be prepared in such a way that an optimal reinforcement arrangement is obtained in the simplest way which is in accordance with the basic assumptions and the design principles. To produce the most economic design procedures, it is necessary to develop different methods for different reinforcement arrangements which correspond to different combinations of acting effects.

For members subjected to *prevailing bending in the plane of symmetry* (pure bending or compound bending with large eccentricities), the optimal reinforcement arrangement is to use either no compressive reinforcement ($A_{s2} = 0$) or less compressive reinforcement than tension reinforcement ($A_{s2} < A_{s1}$). For pure bending, the ultimate moment of resistance M_u of a cross-section can generally be presented diagrammatically as a function of the lever arm of the internal forces (z) and the strains at the level of the steel (ϵ_{s1}, ϵ_{s2}).

For practical use, it is more convenient to tabulate the ultimate moment of resistance as a function of the reinforcement, or to derive simple approximation formulae from the basic assumptions.

For composite bending the same procedure can be used if the bending moment and the axial forces are transformed into equivalent moments and forces acting at the level of the tension steel (see Fig. 3.2).

Figure 3.2   Internal and external forces acting on a cross-section

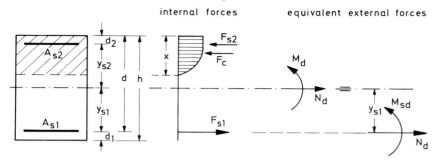

$$M_{sd} = M_d - N_d y_{s1} \qquad (3.3)$$

The required reinforcement is then given as a function of the bending moment M_{sd}.

From an economical point of view it is advisable to use compressive reinforcement if the acting bending moment M_{sd} is larger than a value M_{lim}. The value M_{lim} must be chosen in such a way that an optimum use of the tension reinforcement as well as of the concrete in compression is reached. If the acting bending moment M_{sd} is larger than the bending moment M_{lim} corresponding to x_{lim} (M_{lim}), the total reinforcement is minimized by using some compressive reinforcement. The minimum area is thus obtained by fixing the neutral axis depth equal to x_{lim} and designing compressive and extra tensile reinforcement to sustain the moment ΔM_{sd} where

$$\Delta M_{sd} = M_{sd} - M_{lim} \qquad (3.4)$$

These steel areas are given by

$$A_{s2} = \Delta A_{s1} = \frac{\Delta M_{sd}}{f_{yd}\,(d-d_2)} \qquad (3.5)$$

Design charts, tables, formulae and approximate design methods for sections subjected to prevailing bending are given in 3.2.1 and 3.2.2 for rectangular and T-sections respectively.

For members under *prevailing compression in the plane of symmetry* (axial compression forces with small eccentricities) it is advisable to use symmetrical reinforcement. The bearing capacity of sections with a given distribution of reinforcement under moments and axial forces can be clearly presented in interaction diagrams. Interaction diagrams for rectangular and circular cross-sections with symmetrical reinforcement are given in 3.3.1.1 and 3.3.2.1. On the basis of the interaction diagrams simple approximate formulae can be derived which give results which agree very closely with those obtained using more rigorous methods. Such formulae for rectangular and circular cross-sections are given in 3.3.1.2 and 3.3.2.2.

To design members under *prevailing tension* (axial tension forces with small eccentricities) two different cases have to be distinguished. If the eccentricity of the tensile force $(e = M/N)$ is larger than the distance between the centre of gravity and the level of reinforcement (y_s), a compressive zone develops and the design can be done in the same way as the design of members under prevailing bending. If the eccentricity e is smaller than y_s, all the section is in tension and the bearing capacity depends only on the area of steel. Formulae for determining the necessary reinforcement are given in 3.4.

For members subjected to *biaxial action-effects* (M_y, M_z, N) the optimal distribution of reinforcement depends on the biaxial eccentricity of the action-effects. The bearing capacity can be presented in diagrams which show the necessary reinforcement as a function of M_y, M_z and N for given arrangements of reinforcement. Diagrams for rectangular cross-sections with different reinforcement arrangements are given in 3.5. Approximate formulae for symmetrical reinforcement are also given in 3.5. CEB-Bulletin No. 83 [7] presents a method for finding the optimal arrangement of steel for all values of M_y, M_z, N.

Figure 3.3 summarizes the design procedures for reinforced concrete sections described in this manual.

The various design methods are illustrated by various numerical examples.

13

Figure 3.3   Index of design methods for reinforced concrete sections given in this manual

Action-effect		Cross-section	Design method		
			Diagram	Table	Formula
			in chapter:		
uniaxial	prevailing bending	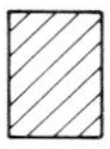 ▨	3.2.1.2	3.2.1.3	3.2.1.4
		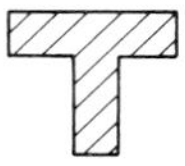 ⊤		3.2.2.1	3.2.2.2
	prevailing compression	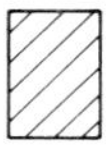 ▨	3.3.1.1		3.3.1.2
		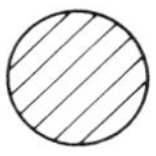 ⊘	3.3.2.1		3.3.2.2
	prevailing tension	for all sections			3.4
biaxial	bending and compression	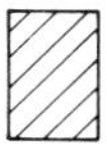 ▨	3.5.1		3.5.2
	prevailing tension	for all sections			3.4

3.2   PREVAILING BENDING IN THE PLANE OF SYMMETRY

3.2.1   Rectangular cross-sections

3.2.1.1   Preliminary considerations on the reinforcement distribution

The optimal (minimum) amount of reinforcement for rectangular cross-sections is in most cases obtained if only tensile reinforcement is used. Only if the bending moment M_{sd} with respect to the tensile reinforcement

$$M_{sd} = M_d - N_d \cdot y_s \qquad (3.6)$$

is larger than the bending moment M_{lim}, the use of compression reinforcement leads to a smaller amount of reinforcement. For a rectangular cross-section, M_{lim} can be derived analytically

$$M_{lim} = 0.688 \, x \, (1 - 0.416 \, x/d) \, bdf_{cd} \qquad (3.7)$$

where the height x of the compression zone is the smaller of the values

$$x_{lim} = \frac{3.50}{3.50 + \epsilon_{yd}} \cdot d \qquad (3.8a)$$

$$x_{lim} = 0.601 \cdot d \left(1 - \frac{d_2}{d}\right) \qquad (3.8b)$$

with ϵ_{yd} = design yield strain of tensile reinforcement.

The results of these formulae are also shown in Fig. 3.4.

Figure 3.4   Reduced bending moment μ_{lim} as a function of the relative cover of the compression reinforcement

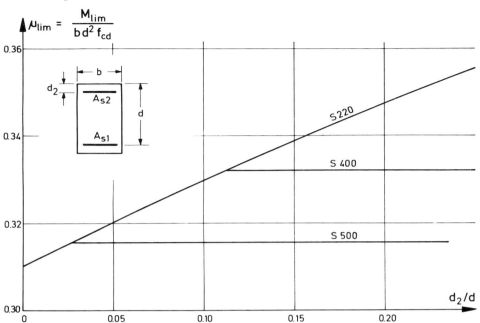

3.2.1.2   *General diagram*

Scope   The general diagram (Design Chart 1) can be used to design rectangular sections in simple or composite bending. As all variables are given in non-dimensional form, all reinforcement and concrete grades and all possible dimensions b and h of the rectangular cross-section can be treated. The diagram can be used for any steel stress–strain relationship and any set of partial safety coefficients.

The diagram shows in a direct, graphical form the relationship between the principal variables involved in a bending problem. For practical use, the General Table (see 3.2.1.3) may be more convenient because it yields more accurate solutions and does not require the determination of steel stresses.

Use   Firstly, the reduced design bending moment μ_{sd} with respect to the tension reinforcement is calculated:

$$\mu_{\text{sd}} = \frac{M_{\text{sd}}}{b\, d^2\, f_{\text{cd}}} \tag{3.9}$$

with: $M_{\text{sd}} = M_d - N_d \left(\dfrac{h}{2} - d_1 \right)$.

Then, it should be checked whether compression steel is needed to obtain the minimum total amount of steel. This can be done by comparing μ_{sd} with μ_{lim} (see Fig. 3.4 in 3.2.1.1). If μ_{sd} is larger than μ_{lim}, compression reinforcement is needed.

Entering with μ_{sd} into the General Diagram, the relative values of the neutral axis depth ξ, the lever arm of internal forces ζ, the resultant of the concrete stresses ν_{c}, the concrete strain ϵ_{c2} and the reinforcement strains ϵ_{s1} and ϵ_{s2} can be obtained. The reinforcement stresses σ_{s1} and σ_{s2} are found from the strains by using the appropriate stress–strain relationships for the type and grade of steel used (see 2.3.4).

If only tension reinforcement is used ($\mu_{\text{sd}} \leqslant \mu_{\text{lim}}$), the required amount of reinforcement can be calculated from

$$A_{\text{s1}} = \frac{1}{\sigma_{\text{s1}}} \left(\frac{M_{\text{sd}}}{z} + N_d \right) \tag{3.10a}$$

If compression reinforcement is required ($\mu_{\text{sd}} > \mu_{\text{lim}}$), the General Diagram is entered with μ_{lim} and the values ζ, ϵ_{s1} and ϵ_{s2} are obtained. The required amount of reinforcement can be calculated from

Design Chart 1 General diagram for the design of rectangular cross-sections

$$A_{s1} = \frac{1}{\sigma_{s1}} \left(\frac{M_{lim}}{z} + \frac{M_{sd} - M_{lim}}{d - d_2} + N_d \right) \qquad (3.10b)$$

for the tension reinforcement and from

$$A_{s2} = \frac{1}{\sigma_{s2}} \frac{M_{sd} - M_{lim}}{d - d_2} \qquad (3.11)$$

for the compression reinforcement.

Example 1

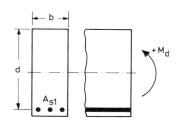

b = 0.30 m γ_s = 1.15 f_{yk} = 400 MPa
d = 0.47 m γ_c = 1.5 f_{ck} = 20 MPa
M_d = 177 kNm

$$\mu_{sd} = \frac{177}{0.30 \cdot 0.47^2 \cdot 20 \cdot 10^3/1.5} = 0.20 < \mu_{lim} \quad \text{(see Fig. 3.4)}$$

No compression reinforcement is needed.

Entering Design Chart 1, we obtain:

ξ = 0.34; ϵ_{c2} = -3.5‰
ζ = 0.86; ϵ_{s2} = 6.85‰

Hence,   z = $0.86 \cdot 0.47$ = 0.405 m.

From the design stress–strain relationship for the reinforcement S400

$$\sigma_{s1} = \frac{400}{1.15} = 348 \text{ MPa} = 34.8 \text{ kN/cm}^2$$

and $A_{s1} = \frac{1}{34.8} \cdot \frac{177}{0.405} = 12.6 \text{ cm}^2$

Example 2

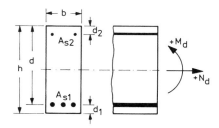

b = 0.20 m γ_s = 1.15 f_{yk} = 400 MPa
d = 0.50 m γ_c = 1.50 f_{ck} = 20 MP
h = 0.55 m
d_1 = d_2 = 0.05 m

M_d = 222 kNm N_d = -200 kN

$$M_{sd} = 222 + 200 \left(\frac{0.55}{2} - 0.05 \right) = 267 \text{ kNm}$$

$$\mu_{sd} = \frac{267}{0.2 \cdot 0.5^2 \cdot 20 \cdot 10^3/1.5}$$
$$= 0.40 > \mu_{lim} = 0.33 \quad \text{(see Fig. 3.4)}$$

From Design Chart 1 ($\mu_{\text{lim}} = 0.33$):

ϵ_{s1} = 1.80‰ ξ = 0.66

ϵ_{s2} = 1.95‰ ζ = 0.72

z = 0.72 · 0.50 = 0.36 m

M_{lim} = 0.33 · 0.2 · 0.5² · 20 · 10³/1.5 = 220 kNm

ΔM_{sd} = 267 − 220 = 47 kNm

From the design stress–strain relationship for the reinforcement grade S400:

$$\sigma_{s1} = \sigma_{s2} = 400/1.15 = 348 \text{ MPa} = 34.8 \text{ kN/cm}^2$$

Required tension reinforcement:

$$A_{s1} = \frac{1}{34.8}\left(\frac{220}{0.36} + \frac{47}{0.50 - 0.05} - 200\right) = 14.8 \text{ cm}^2$$

Required compression reinforcement:

$$A_{s2} = \frac{1}{34.8}\frac{47}{0.50 - 0.05} = 3.0 \text{ cm}^2$$

3.2.1.3 *General Table*

Scope This table can be used for dimensioning or checking rectangular sections subjected to simple or composite bending. If it is used for dimensioning, the minimal total amount of reinforcement ($A_{s1} + A_{s2}$) is obtained. For checking it gives only approximate results if compression reinforcement is used. An exact result can be found by an iterative procedure.

Use The table gives a relationship between the reduced bending moment with respect to the tension reinforcement

$$\mu_{sd} = \frac{M_{sd}}{bd^2 \, f_{cd}} = \frac{M_d - N_d \left(\frac{h}{2} - d_1\right)}{b \, d^2 \, f_{cd}} \tag{3.12}$$

and the mechanical reinforcement ratio

$$\omega = \frac{A_s}{bd} \frac{f_{yd}}{f_{cd}} \tag{3.13}$$

This relationship is based on the parabolic–rectangular stress–strain diagram for concrete and on the bilinear diagram for steel.

The procedures for dimensioning and checking are as follows:

Dimensioning
Firstly, the reduced design bending moment μ_{sd} with respect to the tension reinforcement must be calculated. To obtain the minimum total amount of reinforcement ($A_{s1} + A_{s2}$) it is necessary to determine whether compression reinforcement is required. This can be done by comparing μ_{sd} with μ_{lim} (see Fig. 3.4 in 3.2.1.1). If μ_{sd} is larger than μ_{lim}, it is more efficient to use compression reinforcement.

Design without compression reinforcement
The General Table (Design Table 2) is entered with the reduced bending moment μ_{sd} with respect to the tension reinforcement and the mechanical reinforcement ratio ω is obtained. The required amount of tension reinforcement can be calculated from

$$A_s = \omega \, bd \, \frac{f_{cd}}{f_{yd}} + \frac{N_d}{f_{yd}} \tag{3.14a}$$

A section can still be designed without compression reinforcement if $\mu_{sd} > \mu_{\text{lim}}$, but the total amount of reinforcement will not be the minimum. In this case the General Table is entered with μ_{sd} and the values ω and ϵ_s are obtained. From the stress–strain diagram for the reinforcing steel the steel stress σ_s is determined for the given steel strain ϵ_s. The necessary amount of tension reinforcement is calculated from

$$A_s = \omega \, bd \, \frac{f_{cd}}{\sigma_{sd}} + \frac{N_d}{\sigma_{sd}} \tag{3.14b}$$

Design Table 2 **General table for the design of rectangular sections without compression reinforcement for bending with or without normal force**

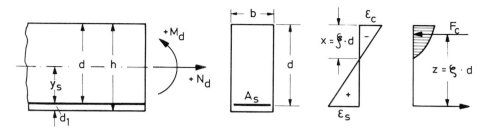

μ_{sd}	ω	$\xi = \dfrac{x}{d}$	$\zeta = \dfrac{z}{d}$	ϵ_c [‰]	ϵ_s [‰]	σ_{sd} [MPa] S220	S400	S500
0.01	0.0102	0.050	0.983	−0.52	10.00	191	348	435
0.02	0.0205	0.072	0.975	−0.77	10.00			
0.03	0.0310	0.089	0.969	−0.98	10.00			
0.04	0.0415	0.104	0.963	−1.16	10.00			
0.05	0.0522	0.118	0.958	−1.34	10.00			
0.06	0.0630	0.131	0.953	−1.51	10.00			
0.07	0.0739	0.144	0.947	−1.68	10.00			
0.08	0.0849	0.156	0.942	−1.85	10.00			
0.09	0.0961	0.168	0.937	−2.03	10.00			
0.10	0.1074	0.181	0.931	−2.21	10.00			
0.11	0.119	0.194	0.925	−2.40	10.00			
0.12	0.131	0.207	0.919	−2.60	10.00			
0.13	0.143	0.220	0.912	−2.82	10.00			
0.14	0.155	0.233	0.905	−3.04	10.00			
0.15	0.167	0.247	0.899	−3.27	10.00			
0.16	0.179	0.261	0.892	−3.50	9.92			
0.17	0.192	0.280	0.884	−3.50	9.02			
0.18	0.206	0.299	0.878	−3.50	8.22			
0.19	0.219	0.318	0.868	−3.50	7.50			
0.20	0.233	0.338	0.859	−3.50	6.85			
0.21	0.247	0.359	0.851	−3.50	6.26			
0.22	0.261	0.380	0.842	−3.50	5.72			
0.23	0.276	0.401	0.833	−3.50	5.22			
0.24	0.291	0.423	0.824	−3.50	4.77			
0.25	0.307	0.446	0.814	−3.50	4.35			
0.26	0.323	0.470	0.805	−3.50	3.95			
0.27	0.340	0.494	0.795	−3.50	3.59			
0.28	0.357	0.519	0.784	−3.50	3.24			
0.29	0.375	0.545	0.773	−3.50	2.92			
0.30	0.394	0.572	0.762	−3.50	2.62			
0.31	0.413	0.600	0.750	−3.50	2.33			435
0.32	0.434	0.630	0.738	−3.50	2.05			410
0.33	0.455	0.662	0.725	−3.50	1.79		348	358
0.34	0.478	0.695	0.711	−3.50	1.54		308	308
0.35	0.503	0.731	0.696	−3.50	1.29		258	258
0.36	0.529	0.770	0.680	−3.50	1.05	191	210	210
0.37	0.559	0.812	0.662	−3.50	0.81	162	162	162
0.38	0.592	0.860	0.642	−3.50	0.57	104	104	104
0.39	0.630	0.915	0.619	−3.50	0.32	64	64	64

Design Table 3 **General table for the design of rectangular sections with compression reinforcement for bending with or without normal force (reinforcement S 220)**

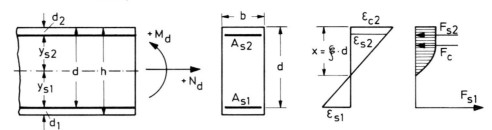

μ_{sd}	$d_2/d = 0.05$		$d_2/d = 0.10$		$d_2/d = 0.15$		$d_2/d = 0.20$	
	ω_1	ω_2	ω_1	ω_2	ω_1	ω_2	ω_1	ω_2
0.33	0.444	0.010	0.455	0.000	0.455	0.000	0.455	0.000
0.34	0.455	0.021	0.466	0.011	0.477	0.001	0.478	0.000
0.35	0.466	0.031	0.477	0.023	0.489	0.013	0.500	0.003
0.36	0.476	0.042	0.489	0.034	0.500	0.025	0.512	0.016
0.37	0.487	0.052	0.500	0.045	0.512	0.037	0.525	0.028
0.38	0.497	0.063	0.511	0.056	0.524	0.049	0.537	0.041
0.39	0.508	0.073	0.522	0.067	0.536	0.060	0.550	0.053
0.40	0.518	0.084	0.533	0.078	0.548	0.072	0.562	0.066
0.41	0.529	0.095	0.544	0.089	0.559	0.084	0.575	0.078
0.42	0.539	0.105	0.555	0.100	0.571	0.096	0.587	0.091
0.43	0.550	0.116	0.566	0.111	0.583	0.107	0.600	0.103
0.44	0.560	0.126	0.577	0.123	0.595	0.119	0.612	0.116
0.45	0.571	0.137	0.589	0.134	0.606	0.131	0.625	0.128
0.46	0.581	0.147	0.600	0.145	0.618	0.143	0.637	0.141
0.47	0.592	0.158	0.611	0.156	0.630	0.154	0.650	0.153
0.48	0.602	0.168	0.622	0.167	0.642	0.166	0.662	0.166
0.49	0.613	0.179	0.633	0.178	0.653	0.178	0.675	0.178
0.50	0.623	0.189	0.644	0.189	0.665	0.190	0.687	0.191

Design Table 4 **General table for the design of rectangular sections with compression reinforcement for bending with or without normal force (reinforcement S 400)**

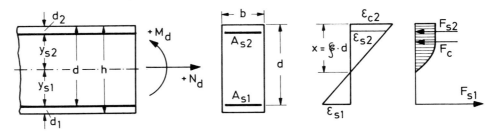

μ_{sd}	$d_2/d = 0.05$		$d_2/d = 0.10$		$d_2/d = 0.15$		$d_2/d = 0.20$	
	ω_1	ω_2	ω_1	ω_2	ω_1	ω_2	ω_1	ω_2
0.33	0.444	0.010	0.455	0.000	0.455	0.000	0.455	0.000
0.34	0.455	0.021	0.466	0.011	0.469	0.010	0.470	0.010
0.35	0.466	0.031	0.477	0.023	0.481	0.021	0.482	0.023
0.36	0.476	0.042	0.489	0.034	0.493	0.033	0.495	0.035
0.37	0.487	0.052	0.500	0.045	0.504	0.045	0.507	0.048
0.38	0.497	0.063	0.511	0.056	0.516	0.057	0.520	0.060
0.39	0.508	0.073	0.522	0.067	0.528	0.068	0.532	0.073
0.40	0.518	0.084	0.533	0.078	0.540	0.080	0.545	0.085
0.41	0.529	0.095	0.544	0.089	0.552	0.092	0.557	0.098
0.42	0.539	0.105	0.555	0.100	0.563	0.104	0.570	0.110
0.43	0.550	0.116	0.566	0.111	0.575	0.115	0.582	0.123
0.44	0.560	0.126	0.577	0.123	0.587	0.127	0.595	0.135
0.45	0.571	0.137	0.589	0.134	0.599	0.139	0.607	0.148
0.46	0.581	0.147	0.600	0.145	0.610	0.151	0.620	0.160
0.47	0.592	0.158	0.611	0.156	0.622	0.162	0.633	0.173
0.48	0.602	0.168	0.622	0.167	0.634	0.174	0.645	0.185
0.49	0.613	0.179	0.633	0.178	0.646	0.186	0.657	0.198
0.50	0.623	0.189	0.644	0.189	0.657	0.198	0.670	0.210

Design Table 5 **General table for the design of rectangular sections with compression reinforcement for bending with or without normal force (reinforcement S 500)**

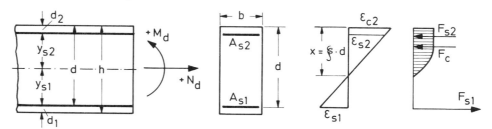

μ_{sd}	$d_2/d = 0.05$		$d_2/d = 0.10$		$d_2/d = 0.15$		$d_2/d = 0.20$	
	ω_1	ω_2	ω_1	ω_2	ω_1	ω_2	ω_1	ω_2
0.32	0.429	0.005	0.429	0.005	0.430	0.005	0.430	0.006
0.33	0.440	0.015	0.440	0.016	0.441	0.017	0.443	0.018
0.34	0.450	0.026	0.451	0.027	0.453	0.029	0.455	0.031
0.35	0.461	0.036	0.463	0.038	0.465	0.041	0.468	0.043
0.36	0.471	0.047	0.474	0.049	0.477	0.052	0.480	0.056
0.37	0.482	0.057	0.485	0.061	0.489	0.064	0.493	0.068
0.38	0.492	0.068	0.496	0.072	0.500	0.076	0.505	0.081
0.39	0.503	0.078	0.507	0.083	0.512	0.088	0.518	0.093
0.40	0.513	0.089	0.518	0.094	0.524	0.099	0.530	0.106
0.41	0.524	0.099	0.529	0.105	0.536	0.111	0.543	0.118
0.42	0.534	0.110	0.541	0.116	0.547	0.123	0.555	0.131
0.43	0.545	0.120	0.552	0.127	0.559	0.135	0.568	0.143
0.44	0.555	0.131	0.563	0.138	0.571	0.146	0.580	0.156
0.45	0.566	0.142	0.574	0.149	0.583	0.158	0.593	0.168
0.46	0.577	0.152	0.585	0.161	0.594	0.170	0.605	0.181
0.47	0.587	0.163	0.596	0.172	0.606	0.182	0.618	0.193
0.48	0.598	0.173	0.607	0.183	0.618	0.193	0.630	0.206
0.49	0.608	0.184	0.618	0.194	0.630	0.205	0.643	0.218
0.50	0.619	0.194	0.629	0.205	0.641	0.217	0.655	0.231

Design with compression reinforcement ($\mu_{sd} > \mu_{lim}$)

In this case the required amount of reinforcement depends on the value of μ_{lim}. Since μ_{lim} is a function of the relative cover to the compression reinforcement and the steel grade (see Fig. 3.4), the General Table has to be subdivided and contains the mechanical reinforcement rates ω_1 and ω_2 as a function of μ_{sd}, d_2/d and the steel grade (Design Tables 3 to 5). The required amount of tension reinforcement is

$$A_{s1} = \omega_1 \, bd \, \frac{f_{cd}}{f_{yd}} + \frac{N_d}{f_{yd}} \qquad (3.15)$$

and of compression reinforcement is

$$A_{s2} = \omega_2 \, bd \, \frac{f_{cd}}{f_{yd}} \qquad (3.16)$$

Checking

To check a given section, the mechanical reinforcement rates ω_1 and ω_2 must be calculated from the given reinforcement areas A_{s1} and A_{s2}. The limit value ω_{lim} can be obtained from

$$\omega_{lim} = 0.688 \, \frac{x_{lim}}{d}$$

with x_{lim} taken from (3.8). Furthermore the difference

$$\Delta\omega = \omega_1 - \omega_2 - \frac{N_d}{b \, d \, f_{cd}} \qquad (3.17)$$

must be determined.

The following cases can be considered:

$\Delta\omega < 0$

In this case there is an excess of compressive reinforcement. Therefore, with sufficient accuracy, the contribution of the concrete can be neglected, giving the reduced resisting moment

$$\mu_{sd} = \Delta\omega \left(1 - \frac{d_2}{d}\right) \qquad (3.18)$$

$0 < \Delta\omega \leqslant \omega_{lim}$

The tensile reinforcement is larger than the compressive reinforcement, but the difference does not exceed ω_{lim}. If the compressive reinforcement reaches the yield limit at the ultimate limit state, the resisting bending moment can be determined for

$$\mu_{sd} = \Delta\mu + \omega_2 \left(1 - \frac{d_2}{d}\right) \qquad (3.19)$$

where $\Delta\mu$ is obtained from the General Table (Design Table 2) as a function of $\Delta\omega$. If the compressive reinforcement does not yield, (3.19) gives only approximate results.

$\Delta\omega > \omega_{lim}$

The tensile reinforcement does not reach the yield limit at the ultimate limit state. An approximation to the reduced resisting bending moment can be obtained from

$$\mu_{sd} = \frac{\sigma_{sd}}{f_{yd}} \left[\Delta\mu + \omega_2 \left(1 - \frac{d_2}{d}\right)\right] \qquad (3.20)$$

where $\Delta\mu$ and σ_{sd} are determined from the General Table (Design Table 2) as a function of $\Delta\omega$.

Examples for dimensioning

Example 3

b $= 0.30$	$\gamma_s = 1.15$	$f_{yk} = 400$ MPa
d $= 0.47$	$\gamma_c = 1.5$	$f_{ck} = 20$ MPa
$M_d = 177$ kNm		

$$\mu_{sd} = \frac{177}{0.30 \cdot 0.47^2 \cdot 20 \cdot 10^3/1.5} = 0.20 < \mu_{lim} \quad \text{(see Fig. 3.4)}$$

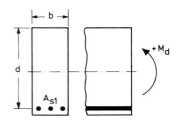

Entering Design Table 2 with $\mu_{sd} = 0.20$ we read $\omega = 0.233$.

$$A_s = 0.233 \cdot 30 \cdot 47 \cdot \frac{20/1.5}{400/1.15} = 12.6 \text{ cm}^2$$

Example 4

$b = 0.20$ m $\quad \gamma_s = 1.15 \quad\quad f_{yk} = 400$ MPa

$d = 0.50$ m $\quad \gamma_c = 1.50 \quad\quad f_{ck} = 20$ MPa

$h = 0.55$ m

$d_1 = d_2 = 0.05$ m

$M_d = 222$ kNm $\quad\quad N_d = -200$ kN

$$M_{sd} = 222 + 200 \left(\frac{0.55}{2} - 0.05 \right) = 267 \text{ kNm}$$

$$\mu_{sd} = \frac{267}{0.20 \cdot 0.50^2 \cdot 20 \cdot 10^3 / 1.5} = 0.40 > \mu_{lim} = 0.33 \quad \text{(see Fig. 3.4)}$$

From Design Table 4 (S400, $d_2/d = 0.10$):

$\omega_1 = 0.533$

$\omega_2 = 0.078$

$$A_{s1} = \omega_1 \, b \, d \, \frac{f_{cd}}{f_{yd}} + \frac{N_d}{f_{yd}} = 0.533 \cdot 20 \cdot 50 \frac{20/1.5}{400/1.15} - \frac{200}{40/1.15}$$

$$= 20.4 - 5.7 = 14.7 \text{ cm}^2$$

$$A_{s2} = \omega_2 \, b \, d \, \frac{f_{cd}}{f_{yd}} = 0.078 \cdot 20 \cdot 50 \frac{20/1.5}{400/1.15} = 3.0 \text{ cm}^2$$

3.2.1.4 Approximate formulae

Scope These formulae can be used for dimensioning rectangular cross-sections subjected to simple or composite bending. Any value of steel or concrete strength can be considered. The formulae are simple and easy to remember. They give a relationship between the reduced internal forces μ and ν and the mechanical reinforcement ratios ω_1 and ω_2.

Use The acting internal forces M_{sd} and N_d are reduced to

$$\mu_{sd} = \frac{M_{sd}}{b \, d^2 \, f_{cd}} = \frac{M_d - N_d \left(\frac{h}{2} - d_1 \right)}{b \, d^2 \, f_{cd}} \tag{3.21}$$

$$\nu_d = \frac{N_d}{bd \, f_{cd}} \tag{3.22}$$

The following cases can be considered:

$\mu_{sd} \leqslant 0.31$
Compression reinforcement is not required. The mechanical reinforcement ratio of the tension reinforcement is

$$\omega_1 = \mu_{sd}(1 + \mu_{sd}) + \nu_d \tag{3.23}$$

$\mu_{sd} > 0.31$
The mechanical reinforcement ratios of compression and tension reinforcement are

$$\omega_2 = \frac{\mu_{sd} - 0.31}{1 - d_2/d} \tag{3.24}$$

$$\omega_1 = \omega_2 + 0.41 + \nu_d \tag{3.25}$$

The necessary amount of tension reinforcement is

$$A_{s1} = \omega_1 \, b \, d \, \frac{f_{cd}}{f_{yd}} \tag{3.26}$$

and of compression reinforcement is

$$A_{s2} = \omega_2 \, b \, d \, \frac{f_{cd}}{f_{yd}} \tag{3.27}$$

Example 5

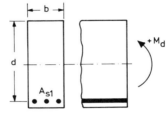

b = 0.30 m	γ_s = 1.15	f_{yk} = 400 MPa
d = 0.47 m	γ_c = 1.50	f_{ck} = 20 MPa
M_d = 177 kNm		

$$\mu_{sd} = \frac{177}{0.30 \cdot 0.47^2 \cdot 20 \cdot 10^3/1.5} = 0.20 < 0.31$$

$\nu_d = 0$

$\omega_1 = 0.20 (1 + 0.20) = 0.24$

$$A_{s1} = 0.24 \cdot 30 \cdot 47 \cdot \frac{20/1.5}{400/1.15} = 13.0 \text{ cm}^2$$

Example 6

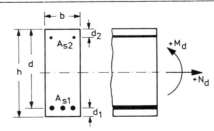

b = 0.20 m	γ_s = 1.15	f_{yd} = 400 MPa
d = 0.50 m	γ_c = 1.50	f_{ck} = 20 MPa
h = 0.55 m		
$d_1 = d_2 = 0.05$ m		
M_d = 222 kNm	N_d = -200 kN	

$$\mu_{sd} = \frac{222 + 200\left(\dfrac{0.55}{2} - 0.05\right)}{0.20 \cdot 0.50^2 \cdot 20 \cdot 10^3/1.5} = 0.40 > 0.31$$

$$\nu_d = \frac{-200}{0.2 \cdot 0.5 \cdot 20 \cdot 10^3/1.5} = -0.15$$

$$\omega_2 \;=\; \frac{0.40 - 0.31}{1 - 0.10} \;=\; 0.10$$

$$\omega_1 \;=\; 0.10 + 0.41 - 0.15 \;=\; 0.36$$

$$A_{s1} \;=\; 0.36 \cdot 20 \cdot 50 \cdot \frac{20/1.5}{400/1.15} \;=\; 13.8 \text{ cm}^2$$

$$A_{s2} \;=\; 0.10 \cdot 20 \cdot 50 \cdot \frac{20/1.5}{400/1.15} \;=\; 3.8 \text{ cm}^3$$

3.2.2 T-beam sections

3.2.2.1 General table

Scope   The T-beam represents a common type of cross-section for members under prevailing bending. In the following, a design procedure for T-beams under uniaxial bending and normal force (neutral axis is parallel to the slab) is illustrated. For the design of T-beam cross-sections under biaxial effects (skew situation of the neutral axis) it is recommended that the reinforcement is calculated iteratively using the rectangular distribution of concrete stresses by estimating the position and skewness of the neutral axis (see 3.6.1).

The design table can be used for dimensioning or checking T-beam sections subjected to simple or composite bending. If it is used for dimensioning, the minimum total amount of reinforcement $(A_{s1} + A_{s2})$ is obtained. If the design table is used for checking, approximate results can be obtained by a similar procedure as described in 3.2.1.3.

It is assumed that the compressive stresses in the flange do not decrease away from the web. For T-beams with a wide flange this assumption may not be valid. In this case, the width b of the flange must be substituted by the effective width b_{ef} (see Appendix 1 of this manual).

Use   The acting design bending moment M_{sd} with respect to the tension reinforcement is calculated from

$$M_{sd} \;=\; M_d - N_d \, y_s \tag{3.28}$$

The internal forces M_{sd} and N_d are reduced to

$$\mu_{sd} \;=\; \frac{M_{sd}}{b \, d^2 \, f_{cd}} \tag{3.29}$$

$$\nu_d \;=\; \frac{N_d}{b \, d \, f_{cd}} \tag{3.30}$$

Design without compression reinforcement

If the value of μ_{sd} is smaller than μ_{lim} which is given in the lower part of the table as a function of the reinforcement grade, the minimum amount of reinforcement is obtained if no compression reinforcement is used. From the design table, the mechanical reinforcement ratio ω can be obtained as a function of b/b_w, h_f/d and μ_{sd} (Design Tables 6 and 7). For input values deviating from those explicitly given in the table, the value of ω can be determined by linear interpolation. The amount of tension reinforcement is calculated from

$$A_s \;=\; \omega \, bd \, \frac{f_{cd}}{f_{yd}} + \frac{N_d}{f_{yd}} \tag{3.31}$$

Design with compression reinforcement

If the reduced bending moment μ_{sd} is larger than μ_{lim}, compression reinforcement should be used. In this case the value ω_{lim} for the reinforcement grade under consideration is obtained from μ_{lim} in the lower part of the design table. Using

$$\Delta\mu \;=\; \mu_{sd} - \mu_{lim} \tag{3.32}$$

the tension reinforcement is given by

$$A_{s1} \;=\; \left(\omega_{lim} + \frac{\Delta\mu}{1 - d_2/d} \right) bd \, \frac{f_{cd}}{f_{yd}} + \frac{N_d}{f_{yd}} \tag{3.33}$$

and the compression reinforcement by

$$A_{s2} \;=\; \frac{\Delta\mu}{1 - d_2/d} \, bd \, \frac{f_{cd}}{f_{yd}} \tag{3.34}$$

Design Table 6 General table for the design of T-beam sections for bending with or without normal force

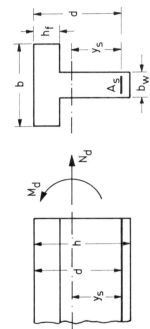

μ_{sd}	$h_f/d = 0.05$ $1000\,\omega$ for $b/b_w =$					$h_f/d = 0.10$ $1000\,\omega$ for $b/b_w =$					$h_f/d = 0.15$ $1000\,\omega$ for $b/b_w =$				
	10	5	3	2	1	10	5	3	2	1	10	5	3	2	1
0.02	20	20	20	20	21	21	21	21	21	21	21	21	21	21	21
0.04	41	41	41	41	42	42	42	42	42	42	42	42	42	42	42
0.06	65	63	63	63	63	63	63	63	63	63	63	63	63	63	63
0.08		91	87	85	84	84	84	85	85	85	85	85	85	85	85
0.10			114	110	107	111	108	108	107	107	107	107	107	107	107
0.12			146	137	131		138	134	132	131	130	130	130	130	131
0.14				166	155			164	158	155		157	155	155	155
0.16				199	179			200	188	179		192	184	182	179
0.18				237	206				220	206			219	211	206
0.20					233				259	233				244	233
0.22					261					261				283	261
0.24					291					291					291
0.26					323					323					323
0.28					357					357					357
0.30					394					394					394
0.32					434					434					434
S220 / S400 μ_{lim}	0.070	0.099	0.138	0.186	0.330	0.106	0.131	0.164	0.205	0.330	0.139	0.160	0.189	0.224	0.330
$1000\,\omega_{lim}$	84	125	180	249	455	122	159	208	270	455	160	192	237	291	455
S500 μ_{lim}	0.069	0.096	0.133	0.178	0.316	0.104	0.128	0.159	0.198	0.316	0.138	0.157	0.184	0.217	0.316
$1000\,\omega_{lim}$	81	119	170	233	424	119	153	198	254	424	157	187	226	276	424

Design Table 7   General table for the design of T-beam sections for bending with or without normal force

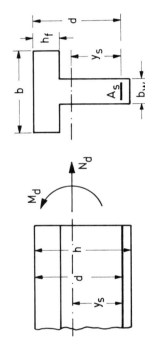

μ_{sd}	$h_f/d = 0.20$ $1000\,\omega$ for b/b_w =					$h_f/d = 0.30$ $1000\,\omega$ for b/b_w =					$h_f/d = 0.40$ $1000\,\omega$ for b/b_w =				
	10	5	3	2	1	10	5	3	2	1	10	5	3	2	1
0.02	21	21	21	21	21	21	21	21	21	21	21	21	21	21	21
0.04	42	42	42	42	42	42	42	42	42	42	42	42	42	42	42
0.06	63	63	63	63	63	63	63	63	63	63	63	63	63	63	63
0.08	85	85	85	85	85	85	85	85	85	85	85	85	85	85	85
0.10	107	107	107	107	107	107	107	107	107	107	107	107	107	107	107
0.12	131	131	131	131	131	131	131	131	131	131	131	131	131	131	131
0.14	154	154	154	154	155	155	155	155	155	155	155	155	155	155	155
0.16	180	179	179	179	179	179	179	179	179	179	179	179	179	179	179
0.18		210	207	206	206	206	206	206	206	206	206	206	206	206	206
0.20			241	236	233	232	232	233	233	233	233	233	233	233	233
0.22				270	261	261	261	261	261	261	261	261	261	261	261
0.24				309	291			293	292	291	291	291	291	291	291
0.26					323				328	323	322	322	322	323	323
0.28					357					357		357	357	357	357
0.30					394					394				396	394
0.32					434					434					434
S220 / S400 μ_{lim}	0.171	0.188	0.212	0.241	0.330	0.228	0.239	0.254	0.273	0.330	0.279	0.285	0.293	0.302	0.330
$1000\,\omega_{lim}$	198	227	265	312	455	275	295	322	355	455	354	367	381	400	455
S500 μ_{lim}	0.169	0.186	0.207	0.234	0.316	0.227	0.236	0.250	0.266	0.316	0.273	0.278	0.284	0.292	0.316
$1000\,\omega_{lim}$	195	221	255	297	424	272	289	311	340	424	343	352	364	379	424

Example 7

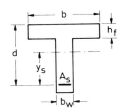

b = 1.25 m	γ_s = 1.15	f_{yk} = 400 MPa
b_w = 0.25 m	γ_c = 1.50	f_{ck} = 20 MPa
d = 1.00 m	f_{yd} = 400/1.15 = 348 MPa	
h_f = 0.10 m	f_{cd} = 20/1.50 = 13.3 MPa	
y_s = 0.58 m		
d_2 = 0.05 m		

b/b_w = 5 h_f/d = 0.10

M_{sd} = 1300 kNm N_d = 0

$$\mu_{sd} = \frac{1300}{1.25 \cdot 1.0^2 \cdot 13.3 \cdot 10^3} = 0.078$$

From Design Table 6, $\omega = 0.082$

$$A_s = 0.082 \cdot 125 \cdot 100 \cdot \frac{13.3}{348} = 39.2 \text{ cm}^2$$

Example 8

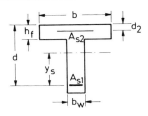

Same materials, cross-section and safety factors as Example 7

M_d = 1500 kNm N_d = -1700 kN

M_{sd} = 1500 + 1700 · 0.58 = 2486 kNm

$$\mu_{sd} = \frac{2486}{1.25 \cdot 1.0^2 \cdot 13.3 \cdot 10^3} = 0.150$$

From Design Table 6:

μ_{lim} = 0.131

ω_{lim} = 0.159

$$\Delta\mu = \mu_{sd} - \mu_{lim} = 0.150 - 0.131 = 0.019$$

$$A_{s1} = \left(0.159 + \frac{0.019}{1 - 0.05/1.00}\right) \cdot 125 \cdot 100 \frac{13.3}{348} - \frac{1700}{34.8}$$

$$= 85.5 - 48.9 = 36.6 \text{ cm}^2$$

$$A_{s2} = \frac{0.019}{1 - 0.05/1.00} \; 125 \cdot 100 \frac{13.3}{348} = 9.6 \text{ cm}^2$$

It should be noted that by a small increase of h_f (from 0.10 m to 0.13 m) the compression reinforcement could be avoided.

3.2.2.2 Approximate formulae for the design of slender T-beams

Scope   The approximate formulae can be used for the design of slender T-beams ($b/b_w \geq 5$) under bending moment and axial forces, if the compression forces can be equilibrated by concrete compressive stresses in the flange alone.

It is assumed that the compressive stresses in the flange do not decrease away from the web. For T-beams with a wide flange this assumption may not be valid. In this case, the width b of the flange must be substituted by the effective width b_{ef} (see Appendix 1 of this manual).

Use The internal stress state is approximated as shown in Fig. 3.5 neglecting concrete compressive stresses in the web. It can be assumed that the reinforcement reaches its design yield strength f_{yd}. After calculating the bending moment M_{sd} with respect to the tension reinforcement from (3.28), the necessary amount of reinforcement A_s can be calculated from

$$A_s = \frac{1}{f_{yd}}\left(\frac{M_{sd}}{d - h_f/2} + N\right) \qquad (3.35)$$

It must also be determined whether the concrete stress σ_{cd} which is assumed to act uniformly over the flange exceeds the permissible value of $0.85\,f_{cd}$:

$$\sigma_{cd} = \frac{M_{sd}}{(d - h_f/2)\,b\,h_f} \leqslant 0.85\,f_{cd} \qquad (3.36)$$

Figure 3.5   Approximation for the internal stress state of a slender T-beam

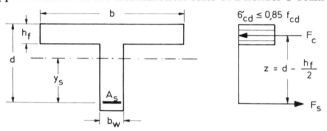

Example 9

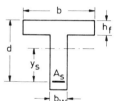

b = 1.25 m	γ_s = 1.15	f_{yk} = 400 MPa
b_w = 0.25 m	γ_c = 1.50	f_{ck} = 20 MPa
d = 1.00 m	f_{yd} = 400/1.15 = 348 MPa = 34.8 kN/cm²	
h_f = 0.10 m	f_{cd} = 20/1.50 = 13.3 MPa	

M_d = 1300 kNm N_d = 0

$$A_s = \frac{1}{34.8}\,\frac{1300}{1.0 - 0.10/2} = 39.3 \text{ cm}^2$$

$$\sigma_{cd} = \frac{1.3}{(1.0 - 0.10/2)\cdot 1.25 \cdot 0.10} = 10.95 \text{ MPa} < 0.85\,f_{cd} = 11.3 \text{ MPa}$$

3.3   PREVAILING COMPRESSION IN THE PLANE OF SYMMETRY

3.3.1 Rectangular cross-sections

3.3.1.1 *Interaction diagrams*

Scope Interaction diagrams (Design Charts 8 to 28) provide a satisfactory solution for designing a section, if the type of section and the reinforcement pattern have already been chosen. This is normally the case for column sections in which the type of section (rectangular, circular, etc.) is known and the reinforcement pattern (usually symmetrical) can also be determined beforehand.

By the use of reduced action-effects (ν, μ), interaction diagrams can be made applicable to sections with any normal load effect (N_d, M_d), any concrete strength and any dimension. But for different values of reinforcement strength and relative concrete cover, appropriate interaction diagrams must be provided. So, usually, a set of interaction diagrams is necessary to cover the expected range of these parameters.

Design Chart 8 Interaction diagram for a symmetrically reinforced rectangular section (S 220; d₁/h = 0.05)

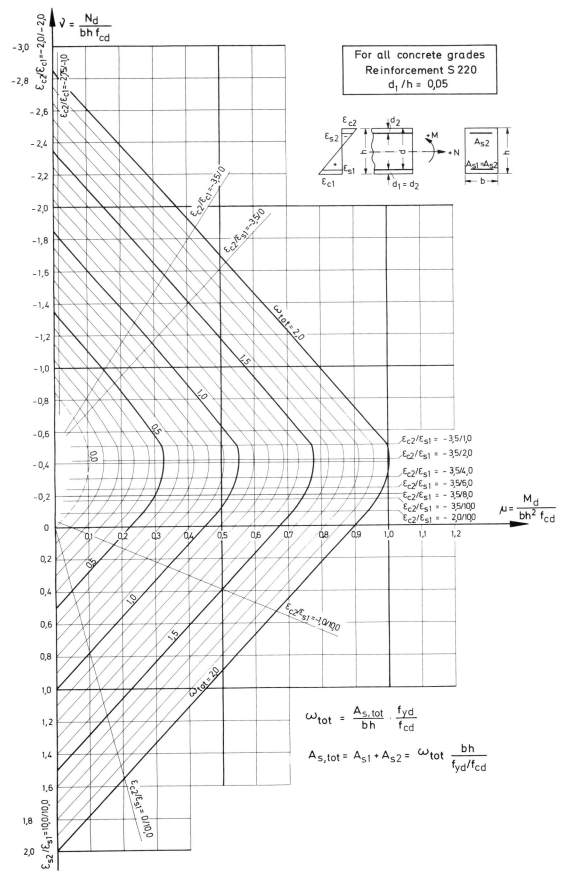

Design Chart 9 Interaction diagram for a symmetrically reinforced rectangular section (S 220; $d_1/h = 0.10$)

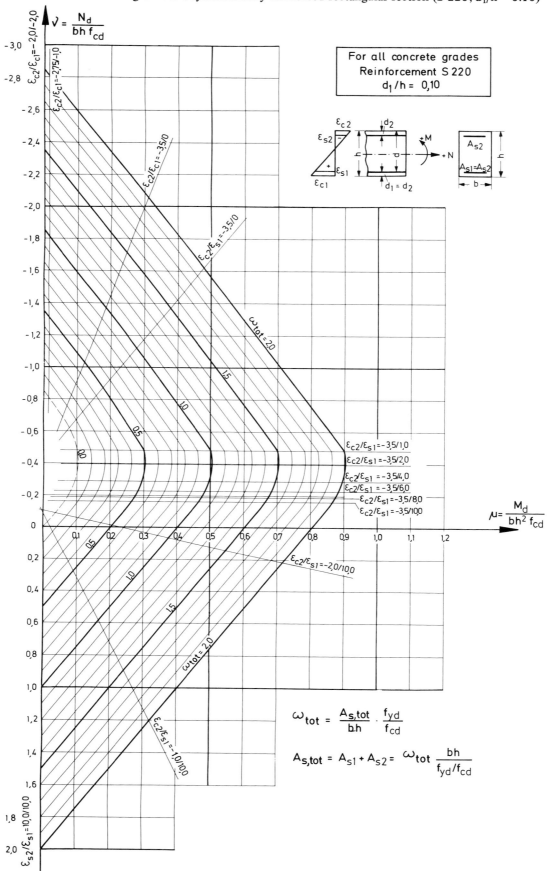

$$\omega_{tot} = \frac{A_{s,tot}}{b.h} \cdot \frac{f_{yd}}{f_{cd}}$$

$$A_{s,tot} = A_{s1} + A_{s2} = \omega_{tot}\frac{bh}{f_{yd}/f_{cd}}$$

Design Chart 10 Interaction diagram for a symmetrically reinforced rectangular section (S 220; d₁/h = 0.15)

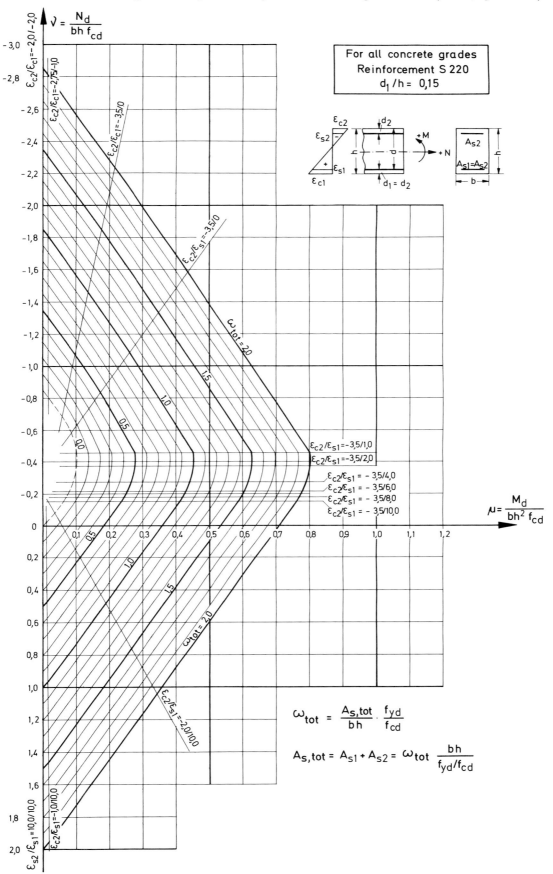

33

Design Chart 11 Interaction diagram for a symmetrically reinforced rectangular section (S 220; d₁/h = 0.20)

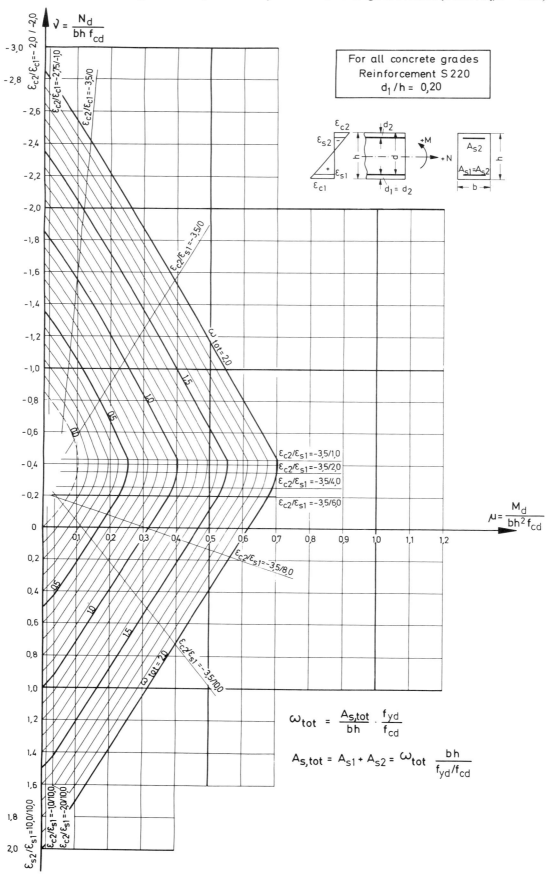

$$\omega_{tot} = \frac{A_{s,tot}}{bh} \cdot \frac{f_{yd}}{f_{cd}}$$

$$A_{s,tot} = A_{s1} + A_{s2} = \omega_{tot}\frac{bh}{f_{yd}/f_{cd}}$$

Design Chart 12 Interaction diagram for a symmetrically reinforced rectangular section (S 220; d₁/h = 0.25)

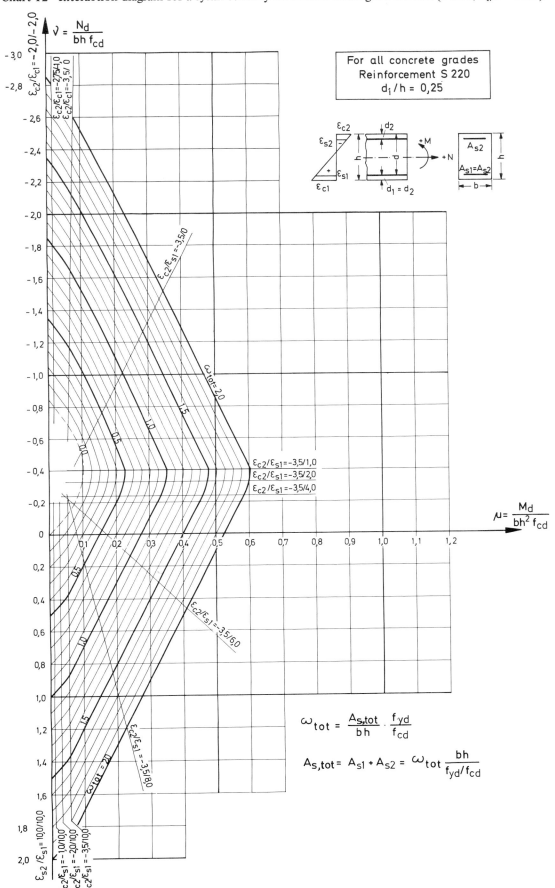

$$\omega_{tot} = \frac{A_{s,tot}}{bh} \cdot \frac{f_{yd}}{f_{cd}}$$

$$A_{s,tot} = A_{s1} + A_{s2} = \omega_{tot} \frac{bh}{f_{yd}/f_{cd}}$$

Design Chart 13   Interaction diagram for a symmetrically reinforced rectangular section (S 400; $d_1/h = 0.05$)

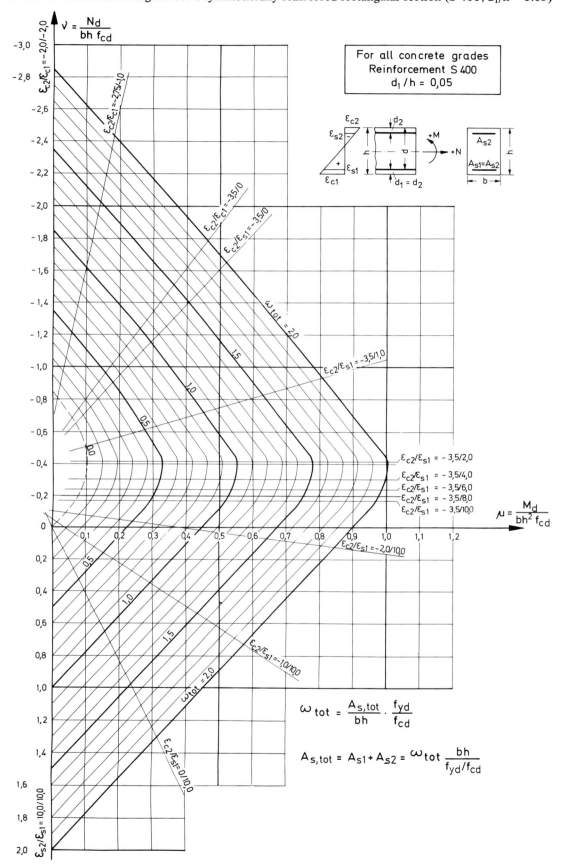

Design Chart 14 Enlargement of Design Chart 13

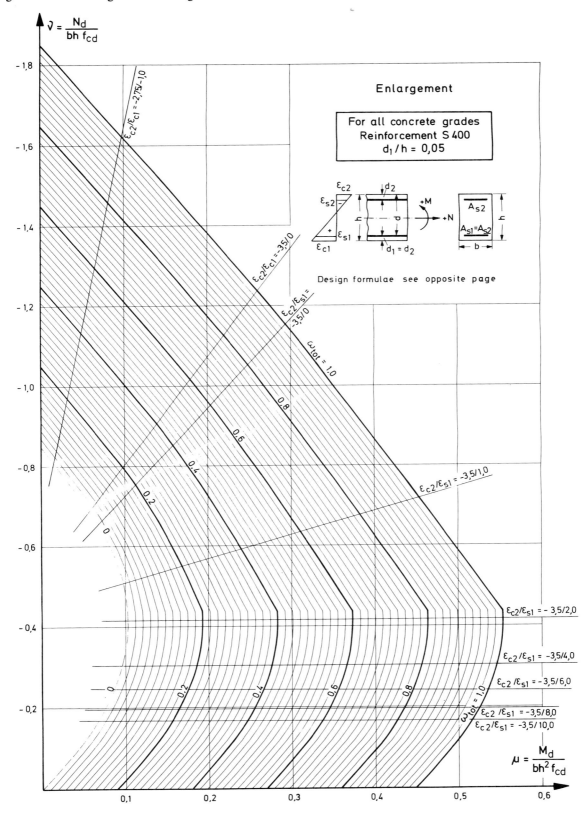

Design Chart 15 Interaction diagram for a symmetrically reinforced rectangular section (S 400; d_1/h = 0.10)

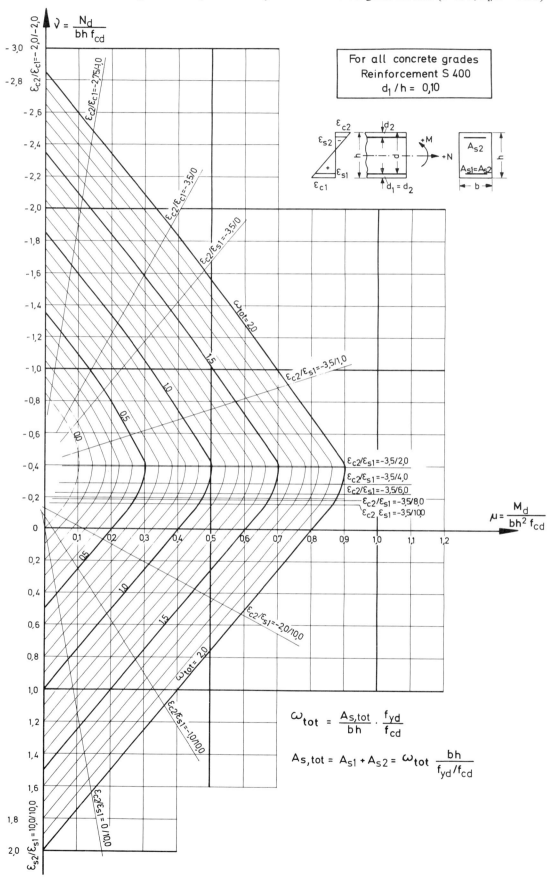

$$\omega_{tot} = \frac{A_{s,tot}}{bh} \cdot \frac{f_{yd}}{f_{cd}}$$

$$A_{s,tot} = A_{s1} + A_{s2} = \omega_{tot}\frac{bh}{f_{yd}/f_{cd}}$$

Design Chart 16   Enlargement of Design Chart 15

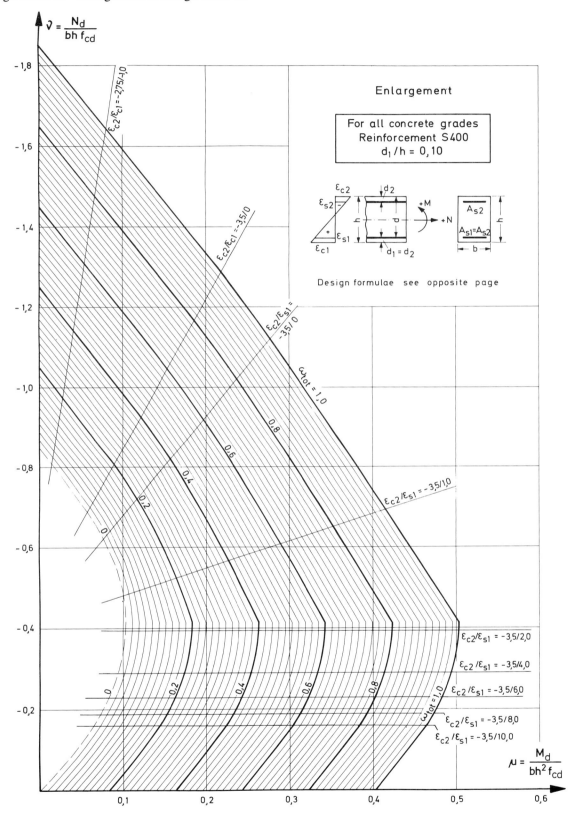

Design Chart 17   Interaction diagram for a symmetrically reinforced rectangular section (S 400; d₁/h = 0.15)

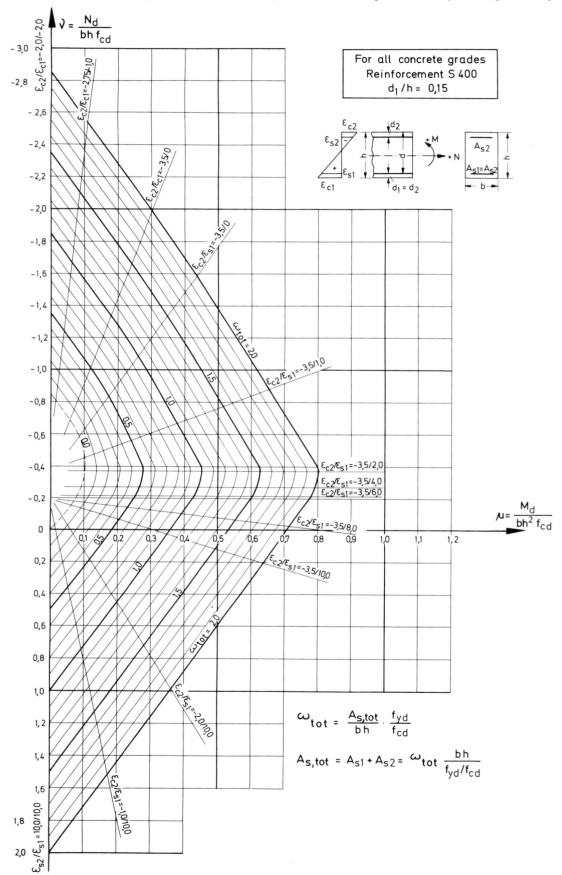

$$\omega_{tot} = \frac{A_{s,tot}}{b\,h} \cdot \frac{f_{yd}}{f_{cd}}$$

$$A_{s,tot} = A_{s1} + A_{s2} = \omega_{tot}\,\frac{b\,h}{f_{yd}/f_{cd}}$$

Design Chart 18   Enlargement of Design Chart 17

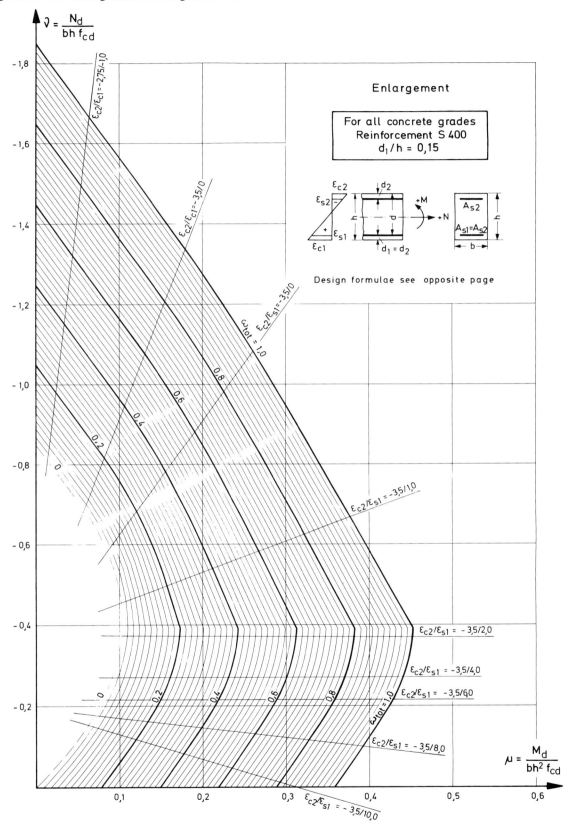

Design Chart 19   Interaction diagram for a symmetrically reinforced rectangular section (S 400; d₁/h = 0.20)

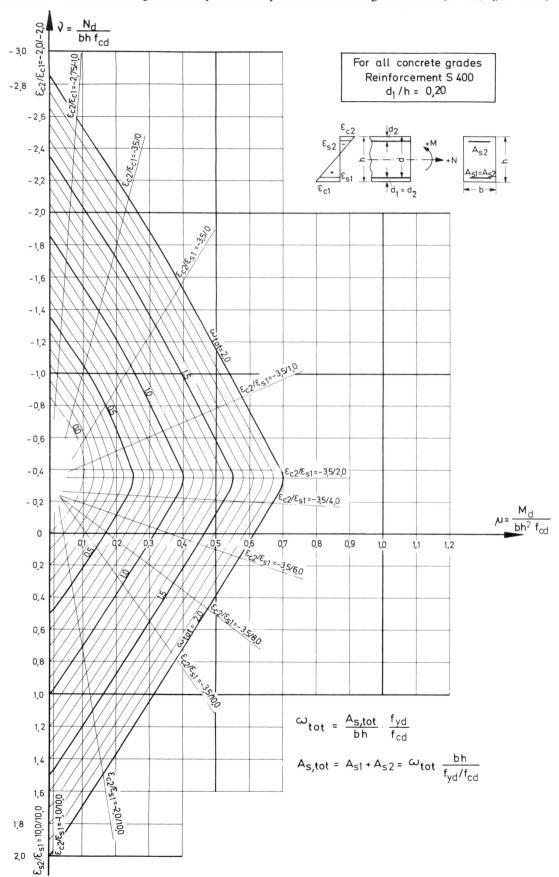

Design Chart 20 Interaction diagram for a symmetrically reinforced rectangular section (S 400; d₁/h = 0.25)

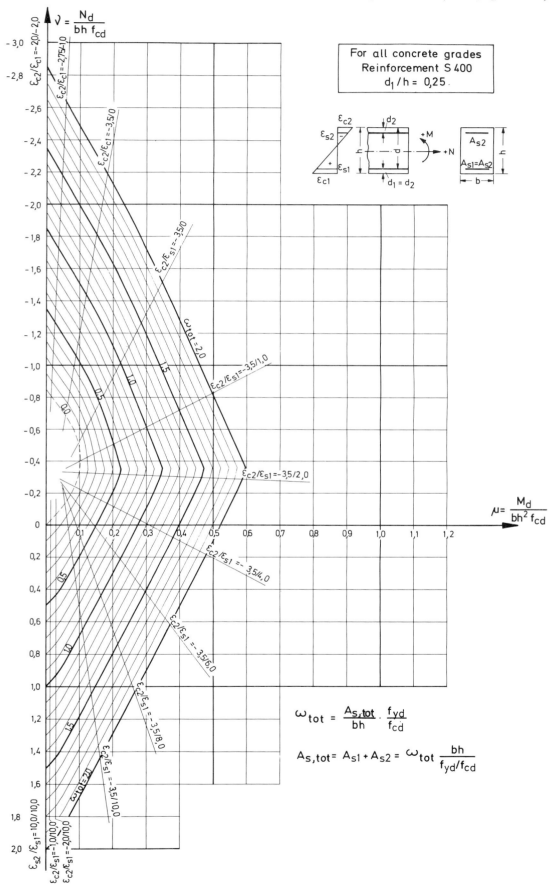

$$\omega_{tot} = \frac{A_{s,tot}}{bh} \cdot \frac{f_{yd}}{f_{cd}}$$

$$A_{s,tot} = A_{s1} + A_{s2} = \omega_{tot} \frac{bh}{f_{yd}/f_{cd}}$$

Design Chart 21   Interaction diagram for a symmetrically reinforced rectangular section (S 500; d₁/h = 0.05)

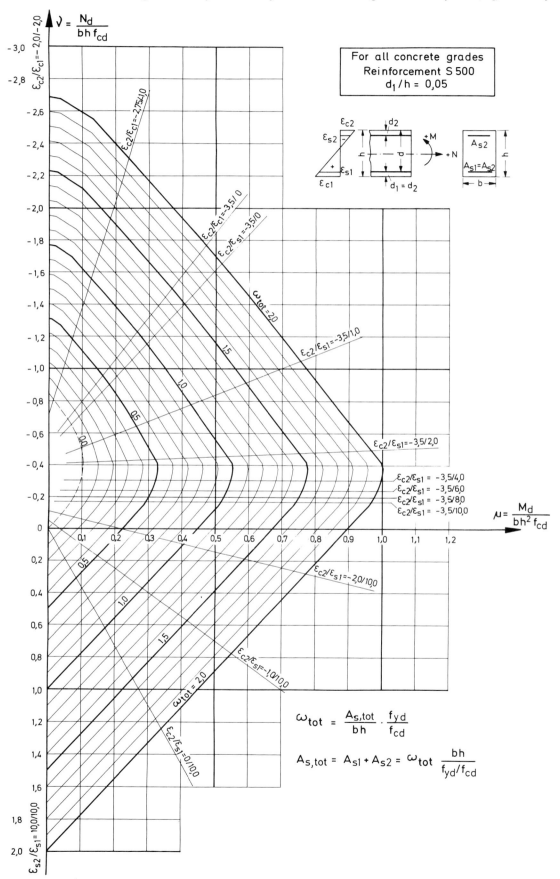

Design Chart 22 Enlargement of Design Chart 21

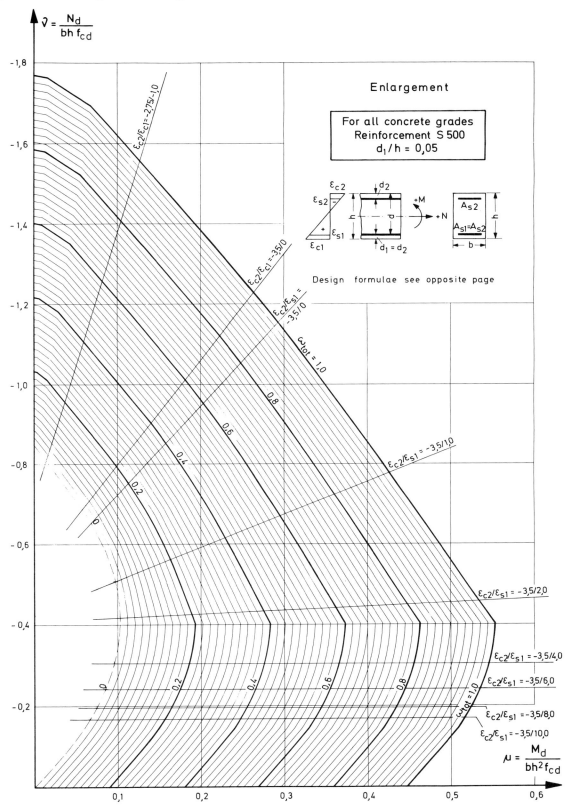

Design Chart 23   Interaction diagram for a symmetrically reinforced rectangular section (S 500; $d_1/h = 0.10$)

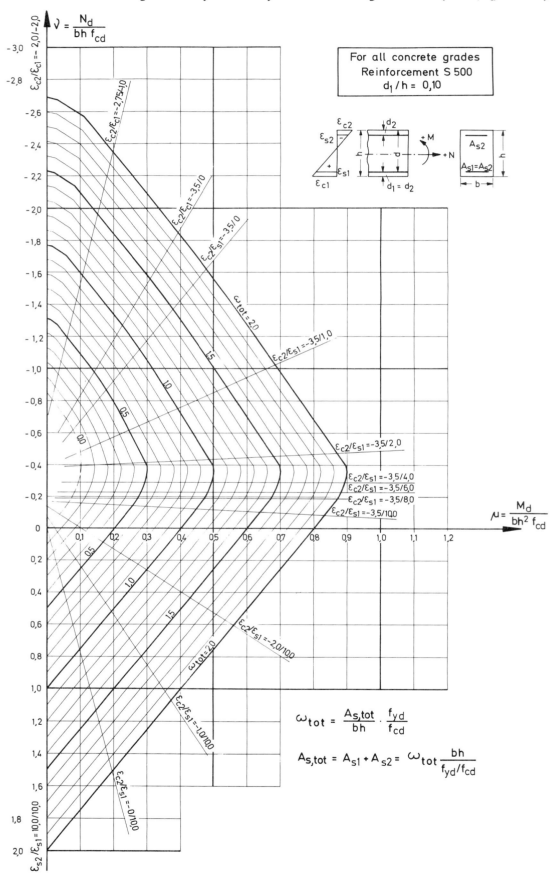

$$\omega_{tot} = \frac{A_{s,tot}}{bh} \cdot \frac{f_{yd}}{f_{cd}}$$

$$A_{s,tot} = A_{s1} + A_{s2} = \omega_{tot} \frac{bh}{f_{yd}/f_{cd}}$$

Design Chart 24 Enlargement of Design Chart 23

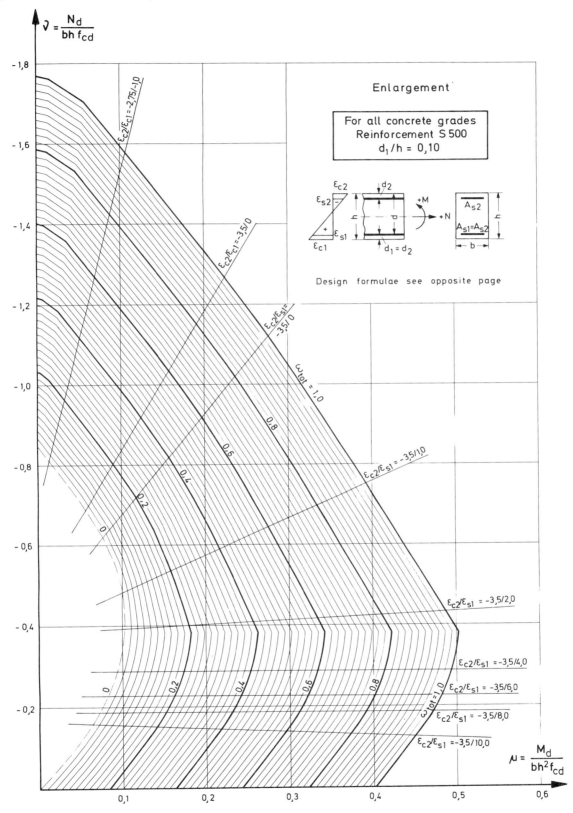

Enlargement

For all concrete grades
Reinforcement S 500
$d_1/h = 0,10$

Design formulae see opposite page

Design Chart 25 Interaction diagram for a symmetrically reinforced rectangular section (S 500; d_1/h = 0.15)

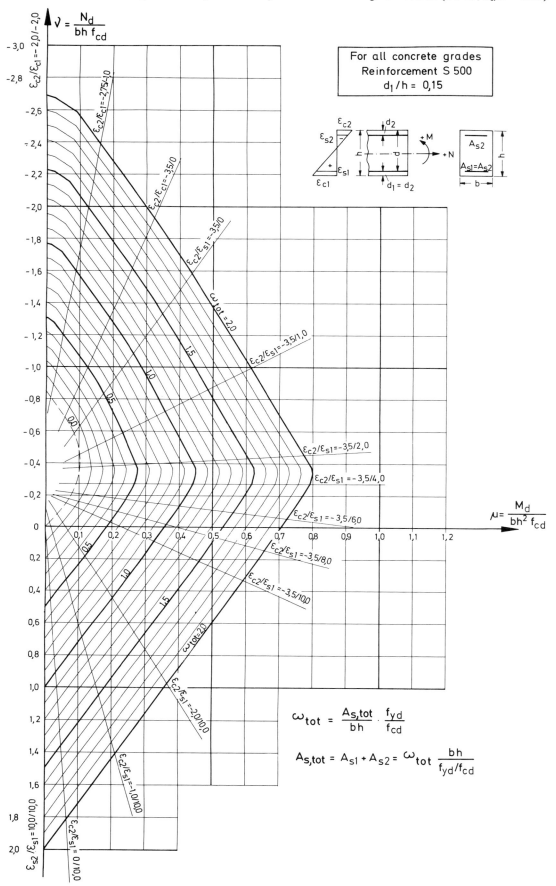

$$\omega_{tot} = \frac{A_{s,tot}}{bh} \cdot \frac{f_{yd}}{f_{cd}}$$

$$A_{s,tot} = A_{s1} + A_{s2} = \omega_{tot}\, \frac{bh}{f_{yd}/f_{cd}}$$

Design Chart 26 Enlargement of Design Chart 25

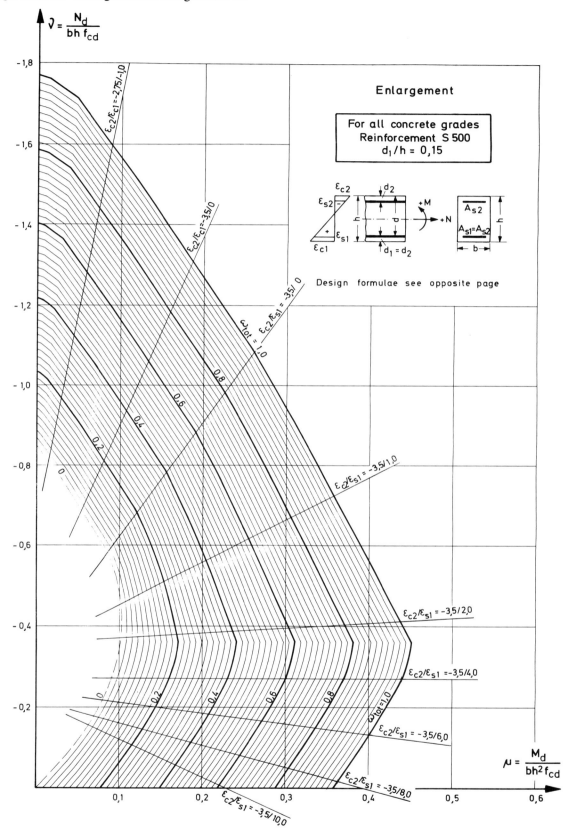

Design Chart 27 Interaction diagram for a symmetrically reinforced rectangular section (S 500; d₁/h = 0.20)

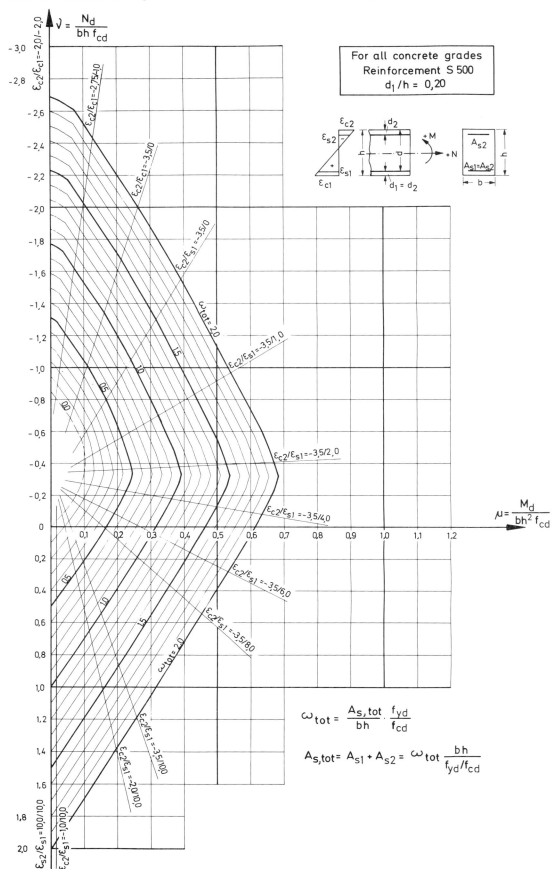

Design Chart 28   Interaction diagram for a symmetrically reinforced rectangular section (S 500; d₁/h = 0.25)

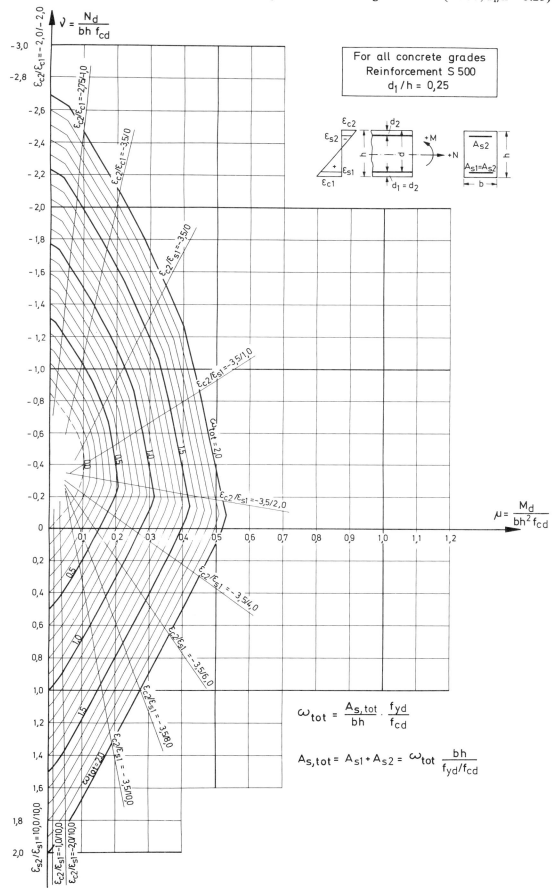

$$\omega_{tot} = \frac{A_{s,tot}}{bh} \cdot \frac{f_{yd}}{f_{cd}}$$

$$A_{s,tot} = A_{s1} + A_{s2} = \omega_{tot}\frac{bh}{f_{yd}/f_{cd}}$$

Use   To determine an exact amount of reinforcement, an interaction diagram prepared for the precise type of section, reinforcement pattern, relative concrete cover and reinforcement grade must be available. A safe estimation of the required reinforcement can be obtained by using an interaction diagram with a higher relative concrete cover d_1/h and/or higher characteristic reinforcement strength.

The reduced action-effects with respect to the centroid

$$\nu = \frac{N_d}{b\,h\,f_{cd}} \tag{3.37}$$

$$\mu = \frac{M_d}{b\,h^2\,f_{cd}} \tag{3.38}$$

are calculated from the dimensions b and h of the cross-section, the design concrete strength f_{cd} and the design load effects. In computing M_d for columns, second order effects and additional eccentricities must be taken into account (§14 and §10.4.1.2 of the Model Code).

Entering the interaction diagram with ν and μ, the mechanical reinforcement ratio ω_{tot} is obtained from which the total amount of reinforcement can be calculated

$$A_{s,\,tot} = \omega_{tot}\,\frac{b\,h}{f_{yd}/f_{cd}} \tag{3.39}$$

The interaction diagram gives, in addition, the strain distribution at the ultimate limit state.

Example 10

b	= 0.30 m	γ_s = 1.15	f_{yk} = 400 MPa
h	= 0.50 m	γ_c = 1.50	f_{ck} = 20 MPa
d	= 0.45 m		
d_1/h	= 0.10		

$f_{yd} = 400/1.15 = 348$ MPa $f_{cd} = 20/1.5 = 13.3$ MPa
$M_d = 200$ kNm $N_d = -1100$ kN

$$\nu = \frac{N_d}{b\,h\,f_{cd}} = \frac{-1100}{0.30 \cdot 0.50 \cdot 13.3 \cdot 10^3} = -0.55$$

$$\mu = \frac{M_d}{b\,h^2\,f_{cd}} = \frac{200}{0.30 \cdot 0.50^2 \cdot 13.3 \cdot 10^3} = 0.20$$

From the interaction diagram (Design Chart 15 or 16):

$$\omega_{tot} \simeq 0.33$$

$$A_{s,\,tot} = 0.33\,\frac{30 \cdot 50}{348/13.3} \simeq 18.9 \text{ cm}^2$$

$$A_{s1} = A_{s2} = \frac{18.9}{2} = 9.5 \text{ cm}^2$$

3.3.1.2 *Approximate formulae*

Scope   Approximate formulae can be satisfactorily used for the design of rectangular cross-sections in uniaxial bending, with a symmetrical reinforcement (mainly) concentrated in two layers near the extreme fibres, as is the case for many column sections. The section may be acted upon by any normal action-effect (N_d, M_d).

Compared with the interaction diagrams, the formulae have the advantages of being applicable to any cover ratio d_1/h and to any characteristic strength of steel, at the cost of a small inaccuracy and of being only valid for reinforcement near the extreme fibres.

Use

(a) Compute the values of ν, μ, ν_c, λ and β

$$\nu = \frac{N_d}{b\,h\,f_{cd}} = \text{reduced axial force};$$

$$\mu = \frac{M_d}{b\,h^2\,f_{cd}} = \text{reduced bending moment};$$

$$\nu_c = -0.85 - \nu = \text{complementary axial force};$$

$$\lambda = 0.5 - \frac{d_1}{h} = \text{reduced distance from reinforcement to centre};$$

$$\beta = \text{coefficient that depends on } \nu \text{ (see Fig. 3.6)}:$$

Figure 3.6 Coefficient β as a function of the reduced normal force ν

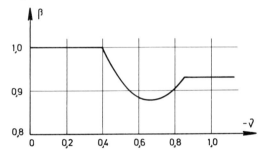

(b) Compute the mechanical reinforcement ratio ω_{tot} by means of the following approximate formulae

if $\nu \geqslant 0$ (tension): $\omega_{tot} = \dfrac{\mu}{\lambda\beta} + \nu$ (3.40)

if $0 > \nu \geqslant -0.85$ (common case): $\omega_{tot} = \dfrac{\mu - 0.55 \cdot \nu \cdot \nu_c}{\lambda \cdot \beta}$ (3.41)

if $-0.85 > \nu$: $\omega_{tot} = \dfrac{\mu}{\lambda \cdot \beta} + \nu_c$ (3.42)

(c) Compute the reinforcement area from the relationship:

$$A_{s1} = A_{s2} = \frac{\omega_{tot}}{2} \frac{b\,h}{f_{yd}/f_{cd}}$$ (3.43)

Example 11

$b = 0.30$ m $\gamma_s = 1.15$ $f_{yk} = 400$ MPa
$h = 0.50$ m $\gamma_c = 1.50$ $f_{ck} = 20$ MPa
$d_1 = 0.05$ m

$M_d = 200$ kNm $N_d = -1100$ kN
$f_{yd} = 200/1.15 = 348$ MPa; $f_{cd} = 20/1.5 = 13.3$ MPa

$$\nu = \frac{N_d}{b\,h\,f_{cd}} = \frac{-1100}{0.30 \cdot 0.50 \cdot 13.3 \cdot 10^3} = -0.55$$

$$\mu = \frac{M_d}{b\,h^2\,f_{cd}} = \frac{200}{0.30 \cdot 0.50^2 \cdot 13.3 \cdot 10^3} = 0.20$$

$$\nu_c = -0.85 + 0.55 = -0.30$$

$$\lambda = 0.5 - \frac{0.05}{0.50} = 0.40$$

$$\beta \simeq 0.90 \text{ (from Fig. 3.6)}$$

$$\omega_{tot} = \frac{\mu - 0.55\,\nu\,\nu_c}{\lambda\,\beta} = \frac{0.20 - 0.55\,(-0.55)\,(-0.30)}{0.40 \cdot 0.90} = 0.303$$

$$A_{s1} = A_{s2} = \frac{0.303}{2}\frac{30 \cdot 50}{348/13.3} = 8.7 \text{ cm}^2$$

3.3.2 Circular and annular cross-sections

3.3.2.1 Interaction diagrams

Scope   Interaction diagrams (Design Charts 29 to 37) provide a satisfactory solution for designing a section if the type of section and the reinforcement pattern have already been chosen. This is normally the case for column sections in which the type of section (rectangular, circular, etc.) is known and the reinforcement pattern (usually symmetrical) can also be determined beforehand.

By the use of reduced action-effects (ν, μ) interaction diagrams can be made applicable to sections with any normal load effect (N_d, M_d), any concrete strength and any dimension. But for different values of reinforcement strength and relative concrete cover, appropriate interaction diagrams must be provided. So usually a set of interaction diagrams is necessary to cover the expected range of these parameters. For the interaction diagrams (Design Charts 29 to 37) a uniform annular distribution of reinforcement is assumed. This is sufficiently accurate provided that at least six bars are provided.

Use   The reduced normal force ν and the reduced bending moment μ are calculated from

$$\nu = \frac{N_d}{A_c\,f_{cd}} \tag{3.44}$$

$$\mu = \frac{M_d}{A_c\,h\,f_{cd}} \tag{3.45}$$

The area A_c of the concrete cross-section is

for circular sections: $A_c = \pi r^2$

for annular sections: $A_c = \pi r^2 (1 - r_i^2/r^2)$

In computing M_d for columns, second order effects and additional eccentricities must be taken into account.

Entering the interaction diagram with ν and μ, the mechanical reinforcement ratio ω_{tot} is obtained from which the total amount of reinforcement can be calculated.

$$A_{s,\,tot} = \omega_{tot}\,\frac{A_c}{f_{yd}/f_{cd}} \tag{3.46}$$

The interaction diagram gives, in addition, the strain distributions at the ultimate limit state.

Example 12 – Circular cross-section

h = 0.50 m	γ_s = 1.15	f_{yk} = 400 MPa
r = 0.25 m	γ_c = 1.50	f_{ck} = 20 MPa
d_1/h = 0.10		

f_{yd} = 400/1.15 = 348 MPa f_{cd} = 20/1.50 = 13.3 MPa

M_d = 200 kNm N_d = -1100 kN

$$A_c = \pi \cdot 0.25^2 = 0.196 \text{ m}^2 = 1960 \text{ cm}^2$$

Design Chart 29 Interaction diagram for a circular section (S 220; d₁/h = 0.10)

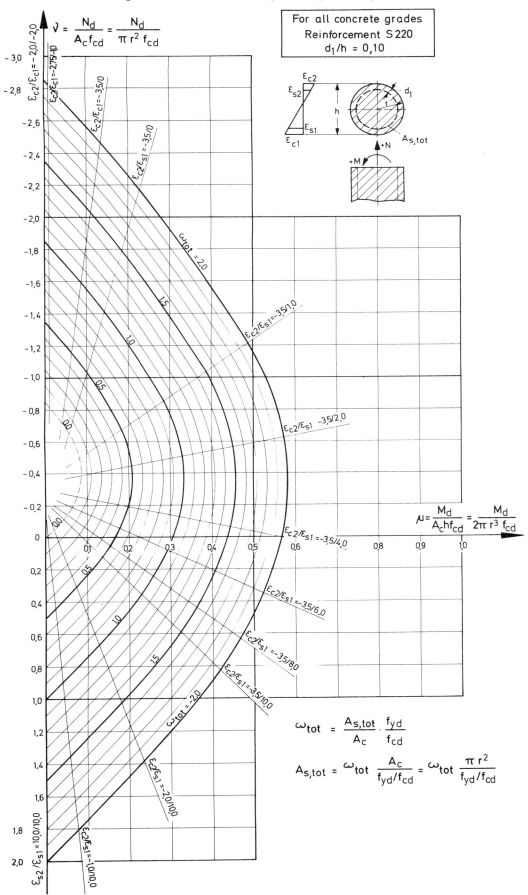

For all concrete grades
Reinforcement S 220
d₁/h = 0,10

$$\nu = \frac{N_d}{A_c f_{cd}} = \frac{N_d}{\pi r^2 f_{cd}}$$

$$\mu = \frac{M_d}{A_c h f_{cd}} = \frac{M_d}{2\pi r^3 f_{cd}}$$

$$\omega_{tot} = \frac{A_{s,tot}}{A_c} \cdot \frac{f_{yd}}{f_{cd}}$$

$$A_{s,tot} = \omega_{tot} \frac{A_c}{f_{yd}/f_{cd}} = \omega_{tot} \frac{\pi r^2}{f_{yd}/f_{cd}}$$

Design Chart 30   Interaction diagram for an annular section (S 220; $r_i/r = 0.70$; $d_1/(r-r_i) = 0.50$)

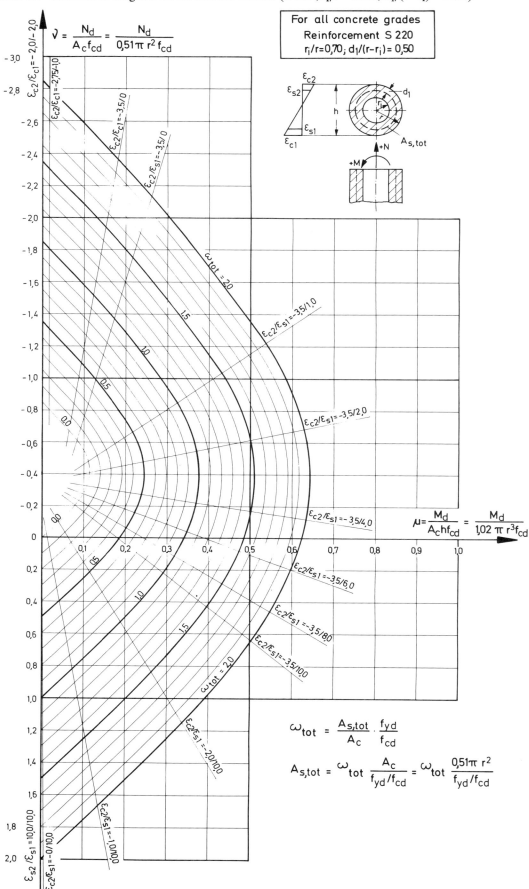

Design Chart 31   Interaction diagram for an annular cross-section (S 220; $r_i/r = 0.90$; $d_1/(r-r_i) = 0.50$)

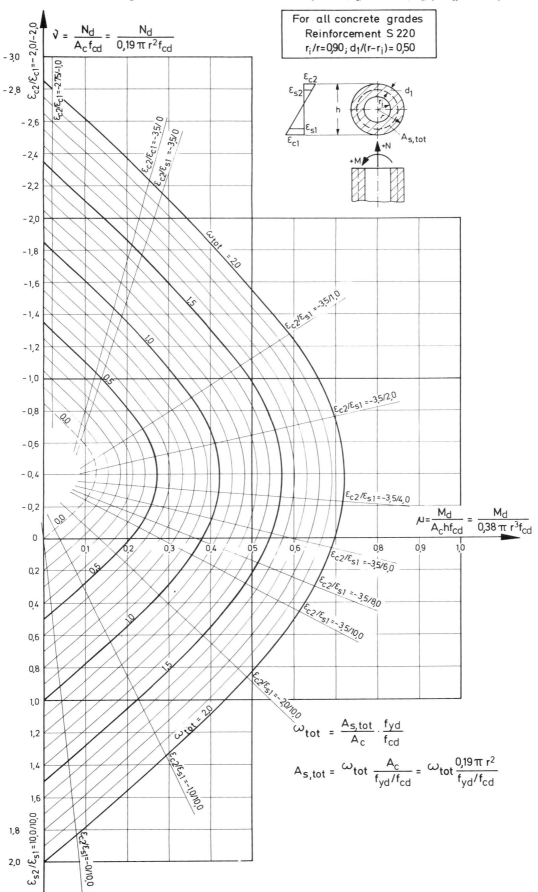

For all concrete grades
Reinforcement S 220
$r_i/r = 0.90$; $d_1/(r-r_i) = 0.50$

$$\nu = \frac{N_d}{A_c f_{cd}} = \frac{N_d}{0.19\,\pi\, r^2 f_{cd}}$$

$$\mu = \frac{M_d}{A_c h f_{cd}} = \frac{M_d}{0.38\,\pi\, r^3 f_{cd}}$$

$$\omega_{tot} = \frac{A_{s,tot}}{A_c} \cdot \frac{f_{yd}}{f_{cd}}$$

$$A_{s,tot} = \omega_{tot}\,\frac{A_c}{f_{yd}/f_{cd}} = \omega_{tot}\,\frac{0.19\,\pi\, r^2}{f_{yd}/f_{cd}}$$

Design Chart 32   Interaction diagram for a circular section (S 400; d$_1$/h = 0.10)

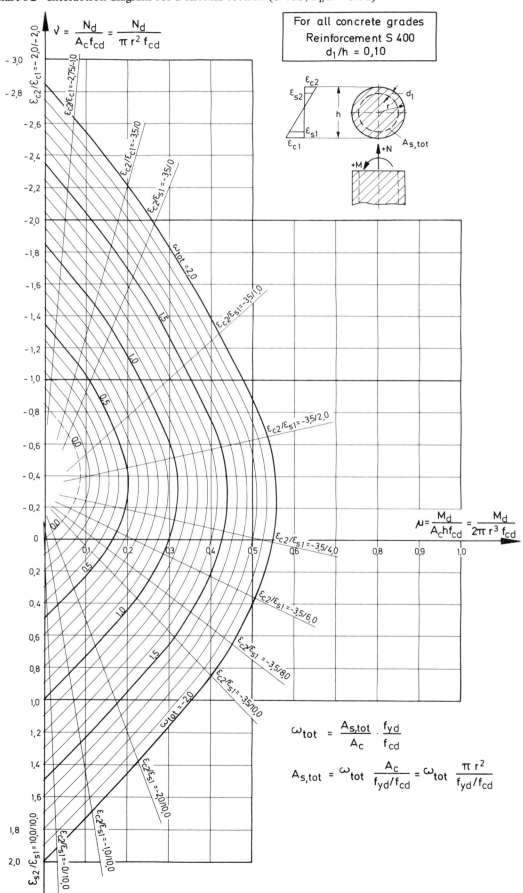

$$\omega_{tot} = \frac{A_{s,tot}}{A_c} \cdot \frac{f_{yd}}{f_{cd}}$$

$$A_{s,tot} = \omega_{tot} \frac{A_c}{f_{yd}/f_{cd}} = \omega_{tot} \frac{\pi\, r^2}{f_{yd}/f_{cd}}$$

Design Chart 33   Interaction diagram for an annular section (S 400; $r_i/r = 0.70$; $d_1/(r-r_i) = 0.50$)

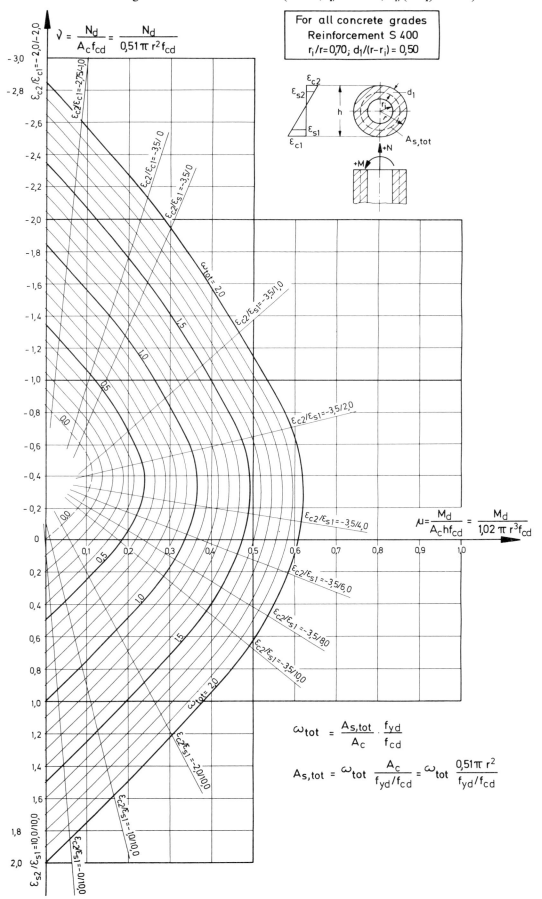

For all concrete grades
Reinforcement S 400
$r_i/r = 0.70$; $d_1/(r-r_i) = 0.50$

$$\nu = \frac{N_d}{A_c f_{cd}} = \frac{N_d}{0.51 \pi r^2 f_{cd}}$$

$$\mu = \frac{M_d}{A_c h f_{cd}} = \frac{M_d}{1.02 \pi r^3 f_{cd}}$$

$$\omega_{tot} = \frac{A_{s,tot}}{A_c} \cdot \frac{f_{yd}}{f_{cd}}$$

$$A_{s,tot} = \omega_{tot} \frac{A_c}{f_{yd}/f_{cd}} = \omega_{tot} \frac{0.51 \pi r^2}{f_{yd}/f_{cd}}$$

59

Design Chart 34   Interaction diagram for an annular section (S 400; $r_i/r = 0.90$; $d_1/(r-r_i) = 0.50$)

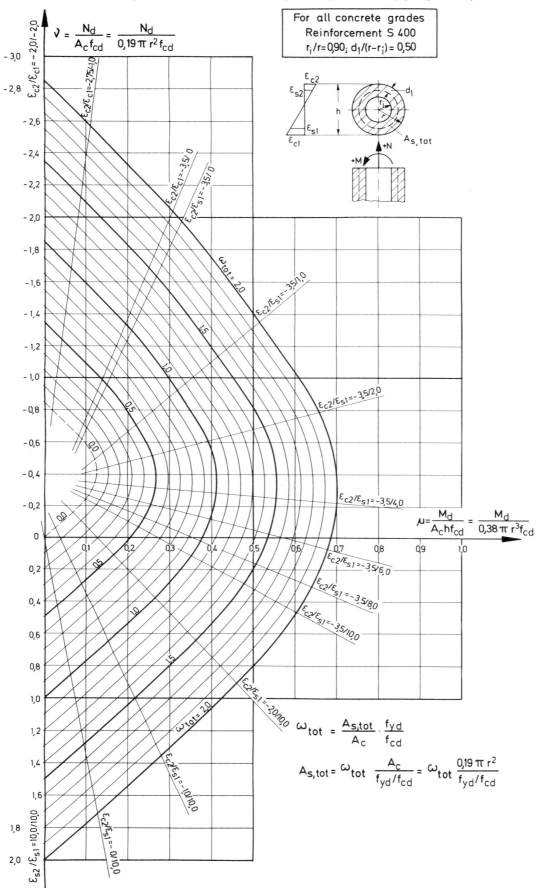

$$\nu = \frac{N_d}{A_c f_{cd}} = \frac{N_d}{0,19\,\pi\,r^2 f_{cd}}$$

For all concrete grades
Reinforcement S 400
$r_i/r = 0,90$; $d_1/(r-r_i) = 0,50$

$$\mu = \frac{M_d}{A_c h f_{cd}} = \frac{M_d}{0,38\,\pi\,r^3 f_{cd}}$$

$$\omega_{tot} = \frac{A_{s,tot}}{A_c} \cdot \frac{f_{yd}}{f_{cd}}$$

$$A_{s,tot} = \omega_{tot}\,\frac{A_c}{f_{yd}/f_{cd}} = \omega_{tot}\,\frac{0,19\,\pi\,r^2}{f_{yd}/f_{cd}}$$

Design Chart 35 Interaction diagram for a circular section (S 500; d₁/h = 0.10)

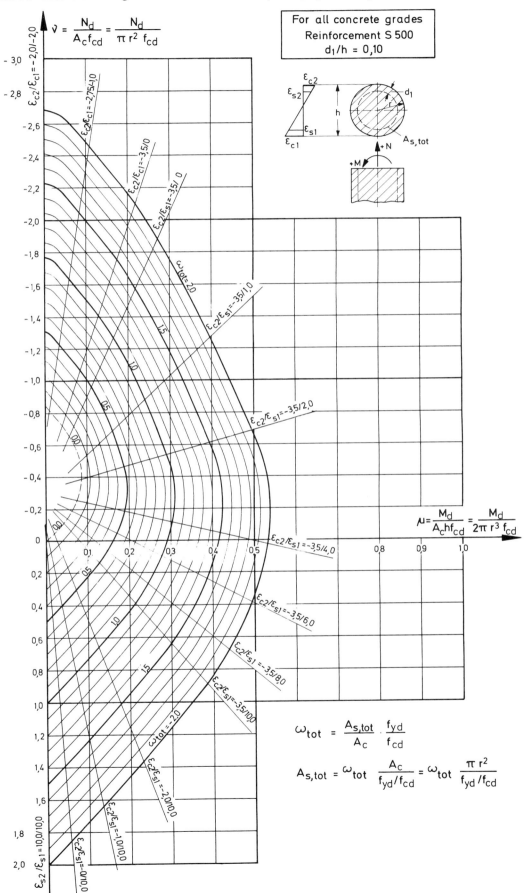

Design Chart 36   Interaction diagram for an annular section (S 500; $r_i/r = 0.70$; $d_1/(r-r_i) = 0.50$)

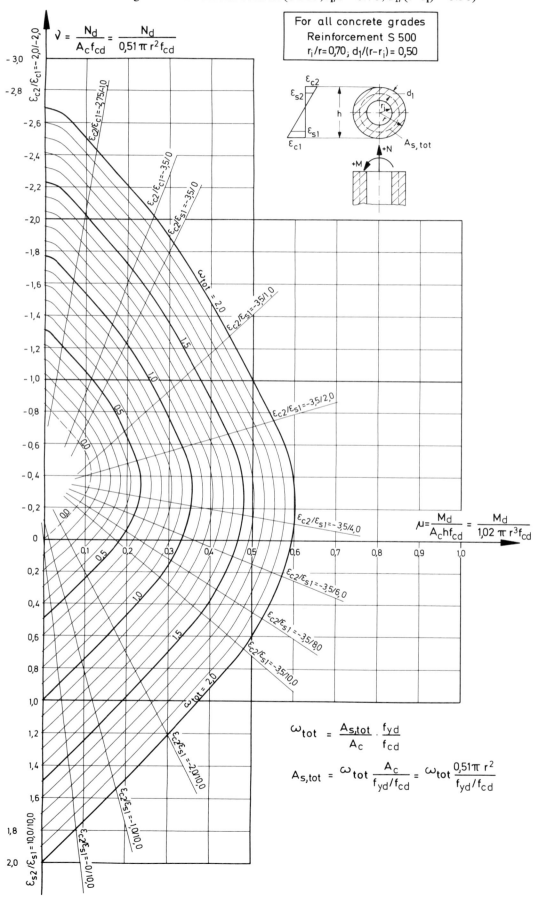

Design Chart 37 **Interaction diagram for an annular section (S 500; $r_i/r = 0.90$; $d_1/(r-r_i) = 0.50$)**

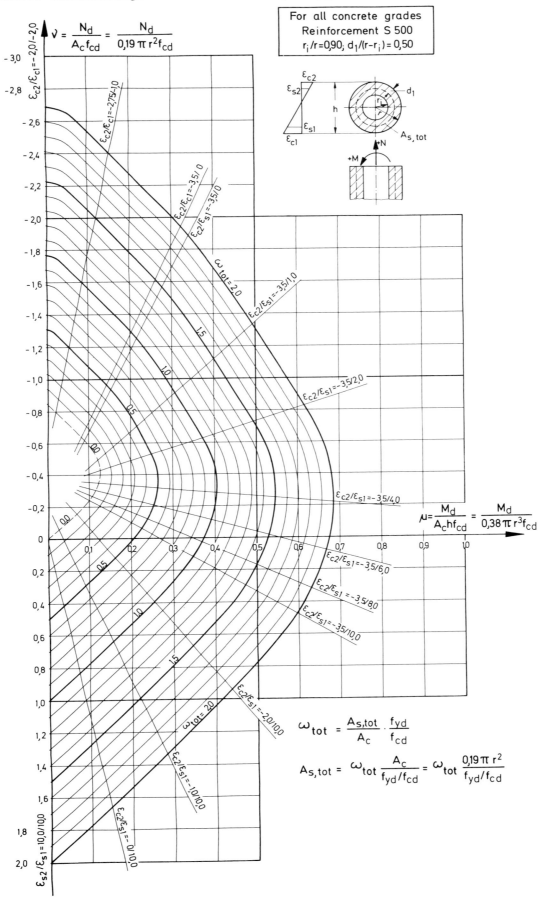

For all concrete grades
Reinforcement S 500
$r_i/r = 0.90$; $d_1/(r-r_i) = 0.50$

$\nu = \dfrac{N_d}{A_c f_{cd}} = \dfrac{N_d}{0.19\,\pi\,r^2 f_{cd}}$

$\mu = \dfrac{M_d}{A_c h f_{cd}} = \dfrac{M_d}{0.38\,\pi\,r^3 f_{cd}}$

$\omega_{tot} = \dfrac{A_{s,tot}}{A_c} \cdot \dfrac{f_{yd}}{f_{cd}}$

$A_{s,tot} = \omega_{tot}\,\dfrac{A_c}{f_{yd}/f_{cd}} = \omega_{tot}\,\dfrac{0.19\,\pi\,r^2}{f_{yd}/f_{cd}}$

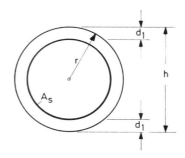

$$\nu = \frac{-1100}{0.196 \cdot 13.3 \cdot 10^3} \simeq -0.42$$

$$\mu = \frac{200}{0.196 \cdot 0.50 \cdot 13.3 \cdot 10^3} \simeq 0.15$$

From the interaction diagram (Design Chart 32):

$$\omega_{tot} \simeq 0.30$$

$$A_{s,\,tot} = 0.30 \, \frac{1960}{348/13.3} = 22.5 \text{ cm}^2$$

3.3.2.2 Approximate formulae

Scope   This formula can be used for dimensioning or checking circular cross-sections subjected to any normal action-effect. Usually it will be employed for the dimensioning of column sections under prevailing compression. It is valid for hot rolled steel with yield stress $300 \leqslant f_{yk} \leqslant 500$ MPa, relative cover equal to 10% of the total depth, and medium values of the mechanical reinforcement ratio ($0.15 \leqslant \omega \leqslant 1.00$), which must be uniformly distributed on a circle. This can be assumed to be the case provided six or more bars are used.

Use   Compute the reduced bending moment and axial force:

$$\mu = \frac{M_d}{A_c \, h \, f_{cd}} \tag{3.47}$$

$$\nu = \frac{N_d}{A_c \, f_{cd}} \tag{3.48}$$

Figure 3.7   Coefficients k_1 and k_2 as a function of the reduced normal force ν

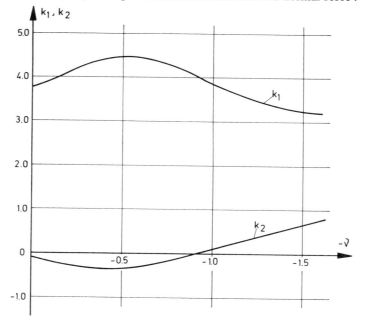

The total mechanical reinforcement ratio is approximately

$$\omega_{tot} = k_1 \cdot \mu + k_2 \qquad (3.49)$$

in which k_1 and k_2 are functions of the reduced axial force given in Fig. 3.7. The total amount of reinforcement required can be calculated from:

$$A_{s,\,tot} = \omega_{tot} \frac{A_c}{f_{yd}/f_{cd}} \qquad (3.50)$$

Example 13 – Circular cross-section

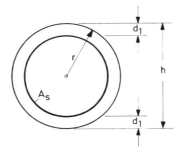

h = 0.50 m	γ_s = 1.15	f_{yk} = 400 MPa
r = 0.25 m	γ_c = 1.50	f_{ck} = 20 MPa

$d_1/h = 0.10$

$f_{yd} = 400/1.15 = 348$ MPa $\qquad f_{cd} = 20/1.50 = 13.3$ MPa

$M_d = 200$ kNm $\qquad\qquad N_d = -1100$ kN

$$A_c = \pi \cdot 0.25^2 = 1.96 \text{ m}^2 = 1960 \text{ cm}^2$$

$$\nu = \frac{-1100}{0.196 \cdot 13.3 \cdot 10^3} \simeq -0.42$$

$$\mu = \frac{200}{0.196 \cdot 0.50 \cdot 13.3 \cdot 10^3} \simeq 0.15$$

Entering Fig. 3.7 with $\nu = -0.42$, we get:

$$k_1 = 4.40 \qquad k_2 = -0.37$$

$$\omega_{tot} = 4.40 \cdot 0.15 - 0.37 = 0.29$$

$$A_{s,\,tot} = 0.29 \frac{1960}{348/13.3} = 21.7 \text{ cm}^2$$

3.4 PREVAILING TENSION

When designing cross-sections under prevailing tension, two different cases depending on the eccentricity e of the axial tension force N_d must be distinguished (see Fig. 3.8).

Figure 3.8 Tension force with small eccentricity

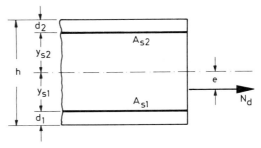

For $e = M_d/N_d > y_{s1}$ a compressive zone develops and the design can be performed with the methods described in 3.2 (prevailing bending).

For $e = M_d/N_d < y_{s1}$ all the section is subjected to tensile strains and the carrying capacity depends only on the area and distribution of the reinforcement. The optimal reinforcement can be computed assuming that all reinforcment is stressed to the yielding strength ($\sigma_{s1} = \sigma_{s2} = f_{yd}$). With the help of the lever-arm principle, the necessary reinforcement can be calculated as follows:

$$A_{s1} = \frac{N_d}{f_{yd}} \cdot \frac{y_{s2} + e}{y_{s1} + y_{s2}} \tag{3.51}$$

$$A_{s2} = \frac{N_d}{f_{yd}} \cdot \frac{y_{s1} - e}{y_{s1} + y_{s2}} \tag{3.52}$$

For a concentric tension force ($e = 0$), these formulae lead to

$$A_{s1} = A_{s2} = \frac{1}{2} \cdot \frac{N_d}{f_{yd}} \tag{3.53}$$

If the tension force acts with biaxial eccentricity or if the reinforcement is distributed arbitrarily over the cross-section, a uniform tensile strain state can be assumed if the point of application of the tensile force lies within the region bounded by the lines connecting the corner reinforcement bars. It can further be assumed that all reinforcement bars reach the design yield stress f_{yd} at the ultimate limit state such that the reinforcement can be determined from equilibrium conditions alone. If more than three bars are used to carry the tension force, obviously an infinite number of solutions exists.

Example 14

b = 0.30 m γ_s = 1.15 f_{yk} = 400 MPa

h = 1.00 m γ_c = 1.50 f_{ck} = 20 MPa

$d_1 = d_2$ = 0.10 m

M_d = 225 kNm N_d = 375 kN

$y_{s1} = y_{s2} = h/2 - d_1 = 0.50 - 0.10 = 0.40$ m

$e = M_d/N_d = 225/375 = 0.60$ m $> y_{s1} = 0.40$ m

The design can be performed with the methods of 3.2:

$$M_{sd} = M_d - N_d \cdot y_{s1} = 225 - 375 \cdot 0.40 = 75 \text{ kNm}$$

$$d = h - d_1 = 1.00 - 0.10 = 0.90 \text{ m}$$

$$f_{yd} = 400/1.15 = 348 \text{ MPa} = 34.8 \text{ kN/cm}^2$$

$$f_{cd} = 20/1.5 = 13.3 \text{ MPa}$$

$$\mu_{sd} = \frac{M_{sd}}{bd^2 f_{cd}} = \frac{75 \cdot 10^{-3}}{0.3 \cdot 0.9^2 \cdot 13.3} = 0.023 < \mu_{lim}$$

Compression reinforcement is not necessary: $A_{s2} = 0$.

From Design Table 2: $\omega = 0.0237$

$$A_{s1} = \omega \, bd \, \frac{f_{cd}}{f_{yd}} + \frac{N_d}{f_{yd}}$$

$$= 0.0237 \cdot 30 \cdot 90 \, \frac{13.3}{348} + \frac{375}{34.8} = 13.2 \text{ cm}^2$$

Example 15

Materials, cross-section and safety factors are equal to Example 14.

M_d = 75 kNm N_d = 375 kN

$e = M_d/N_d = 75/375 = 0.20$ m $< y_{s1} = 0.40$ m

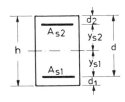

The design can be performed using (3.51) and (3.52):

$$A_{s1} = \frac{375}{34.8} \frac{0.40 + 0.20}{0.40 + 0.40} = 8.1 \text{ cm}^2$$

$$A_{s2} = \frac{375}{34.8} \frac{0.40 - 0.20}{0.40 + 0.40} = 2.7 \text{ cm}^2$$

3.5 BIAXIAL ACTION-EFFECTS

3.5.1 Interaction surfaces

Scope Interaction surfaces are the equivalent of interaction diagrams for skew bending problems. They provide a satisfactory solution for the design of a section in skew bending, if the type of section and the reinforcement pattern have already been chosen, as is usually the case for column sections.

The section may be acted upon by any normal load effect N_d, M_{yd}, M_{zd}. Presented in a non-dimensional form, interaction surfaces are not dependent on the concrete strength or on the dimensions of the cross-section. Each interaction surface is, however, valid only for one section type, one reinforcement pattern, one relative cover ratio and one grade of steel. A two-dimensional presentation of the three-dimensional interaction surface can be provided for any given relative normal force v. If the reinforcement pattern and the section form are symmetrical, not all possible combinations of M_y and M_z need to be considered and the diagrams for several values of v can be presented together (see Design Charts 38 to 53*).

Nevertheless, a whole set of interaction surfaces is required to cover the variation of all the parameters. Approximate, safe design can be obtained by means of interaction surfaces prepared for a reinforcement pattern or embedment ratio for which the reinforcement is relatively farther from the extreme fibres, or for a steel with a higher characteristic strength.

Use The reduced normal force v and bending moments μ_y and μ_z are calculated from

$$v = \frac{N_d}{b \, h \, f_{cd}} \tag{3.54}$$

$$\mu_y = \frac{M_{yd}}{b \, h^2 \, f_{cd}} \tag{3.55}$$

$$\mu_z = \frac{M_{zd}}{b^2 \, h \, f_{cd}} \tag{3.56}$$

It must be noted that for some reinforcement patterns the absolute values of M_{yd} and M_{zd} must be taken to determine μ_y and μ_z.

Before entering the design charts μ_1 and μ_2 must be chosen from μ_y and μ_z in the way indicated beneath the diagrams. Entering the appropriate diagram with v, μ_1 and μ_2, the mechanical reinforcement ratio ω_{tot} is obtained from which the total reinforcement area $A_{s, tot}$ is easily computed

$$A_{s, tot} = \omega_{tot} \frac{b \, h}{f_{yd}/f_{cd}} \tag{3.57}$$

In most cases, the value of v will not exactly coincide with any of the values presented in the diagrams. Then, ω must be obtained by interpolating between the ω values obtained using the diagrams corresponding to the v values next to the particular v under consideration.

---

*These Design Charts have been prepared by D Linse, München.

Design Chart 38 Interaction diagram for a rectangular section under biaxial bending and axial force (S 220; reinforcement arrangement 1)

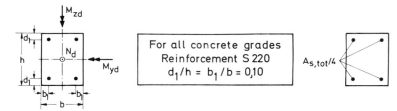

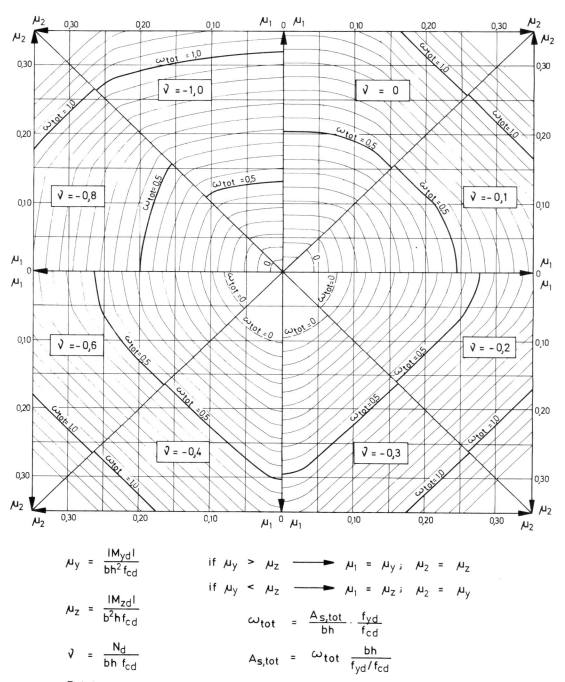

$$\mu_y = \frac{|M_{yd}|}{bh^2 f_{cd}}$$

if $\mu_y > \mu_z \longrightarrow \mu_1 = \mu_y ; \quad \mu_2 = \mu_z$

if $\mu_y < \mu_z \longrightarrow \mu_1 = \mu_z ; \quad \mu_2 = \mu_y$

$$\mu_z = \frac{|M_{zd}|}{b^2 h f_{cd}}$$

$$\omega_{tot} = \frac{A_{s,tot}}{bh} \cdot \frac{f_{yd}}{f_{cd}}$$

$$\nu = \frac{N_d}{bh\, f_{cd}}$$

$$A_{s,tot} = \omega_{tot}\, \frac{bh}{f_{yd}/f_{cd}}$$

Reinforcement arrangement see section at head of the table

Design Chart 39 Interaction diagram for a rectangular section under biaxial bending and axial force (S 220; reinforcement arrangement 2)

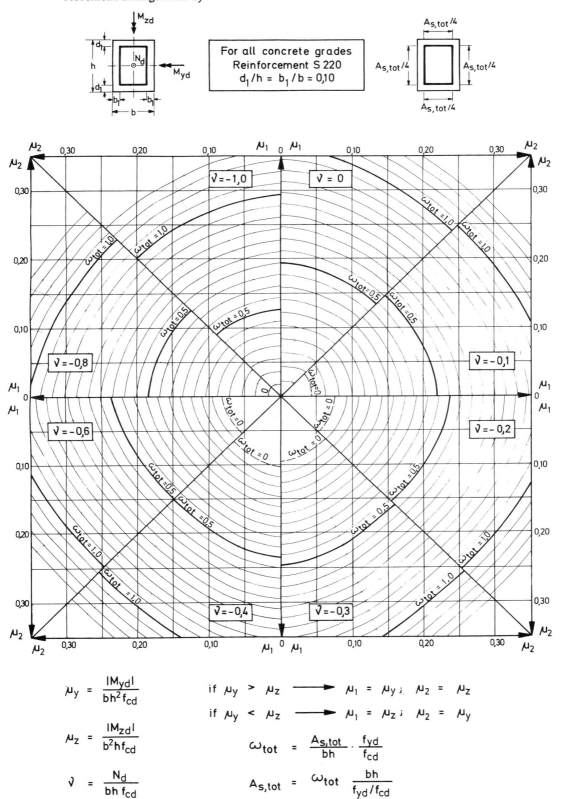

For all concrete grades
Reinforcement S 220
$d_1/h = b_1/b = 0{,}10$

$$\mu_y = \frac{|M_{yd}|}{bh^2 f_{cd}}$$

if $\mu_y > \mu_z \longrightarrow \mu_1 = \mu_y$; $\mu_2 = \mu_z$

if $\mu_y < \mu_z \longrightarrow \mu_1 = \mu_z$; $\mu_2 = \mu_y$

$$\mu_z = \frac{|M_{zd}|}{b^2 h f_{cd}}$$

$$\omega_{tot} = \frac{A_{s,tot}}{bh} \cdot \frac{f_{yd}}{f_{cd}}$$

$$\nu = \frac{N_d}{bh\, f_{cd}}$$

$$A_{s,tot} = \omega_{tot} \frac{bh}{f_{yd}/f_{cd}}$$

Reinforcement arrangement see section at head of the table

69

Design Chart 40 **Interaction diagram for a rectangular section under biaxial bending and axial force (S 220; reinforcement arrangement 3)**

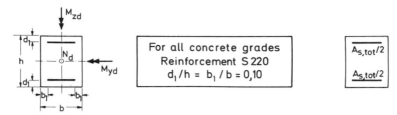

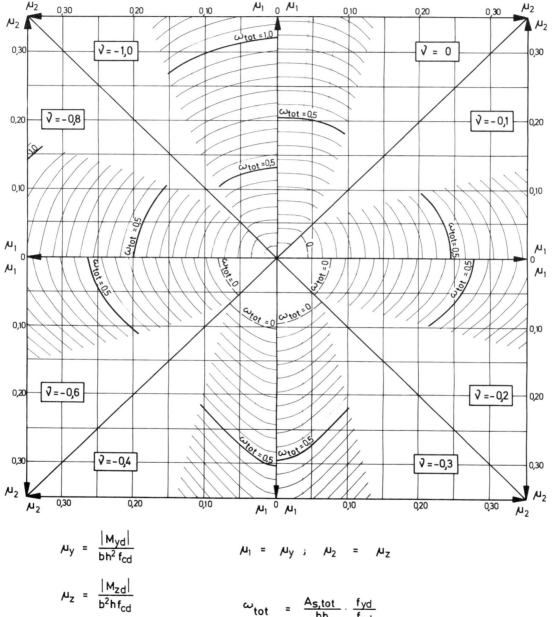

$$\mu_y = \frac{|M_{yd}|}{bh^2 f_{cd}}$$

$$\mu_z = \frac{|M_{zd}|}{b^2 h f_{cd}}$$

$$\nu = \frac{N_d}{bh f_{cd}}$$

$$\mu_1 = \mu_y \; ; \quad \mu_2 = \mu_z$$

$$\omega_{tot} = \frac{A_{s,tot}}{bh} \cdot \frac{f_{yd}}{f_{cd}}$$

$$A_{s,tot} = \omega_{tot} \frac{bh}{f_{yd}/f_{cd}}$$

Reinforcement arrangement see section at head of the table

Design Chart 41 Interaction diagram for a rectangular section under biaxial bending and axial force (S 220; reinforcement arrangement 4)

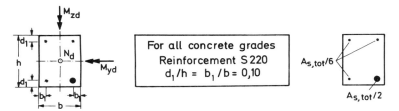

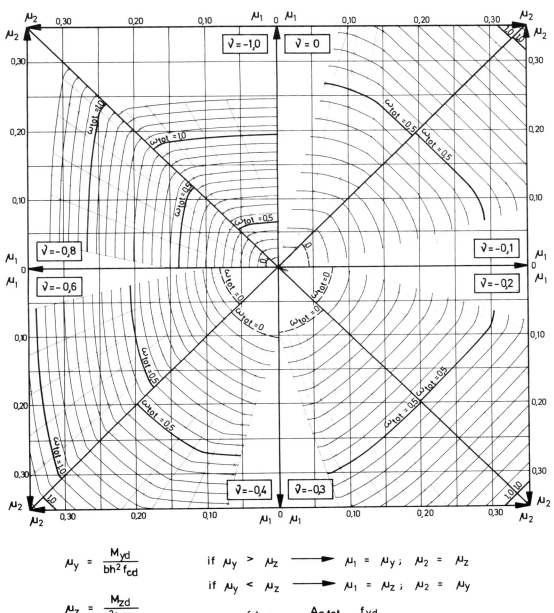

$$\mu_y = \frac{M_{yd}}{bh^2 f_{cd}}$$

if $\mu_y > \mu_z$ ⟶ $\mu_1 = \mu_y$; $\mu_2 = \mu_z$

if $\mu_y < \mu_z$ ⟶ $\mu_1 = \mu_z$; $\mu_2 = \mu_y$

$$\mu_z = \frac{M_{zd}}{b^2 h f_{cd}}$$

$$\omega_{tot} = \frac{A_{s,tot}}{bh} \cdot \frac{f_{yd}}{f_{cd}}$$

$$\nu = \frac{N_d}{bh f_{cd}}$$

$$A_{s,tot} = \omega_{tot} \frac{bh}{f_{yd}/f_{cd}}$$

Reinforcement arrangement see section at head of the table

Design Chart 42 Interaction diagram for a rectangular section under biaxial bending and axial force (S 400; reinforcement arrangement 1)

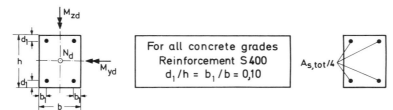

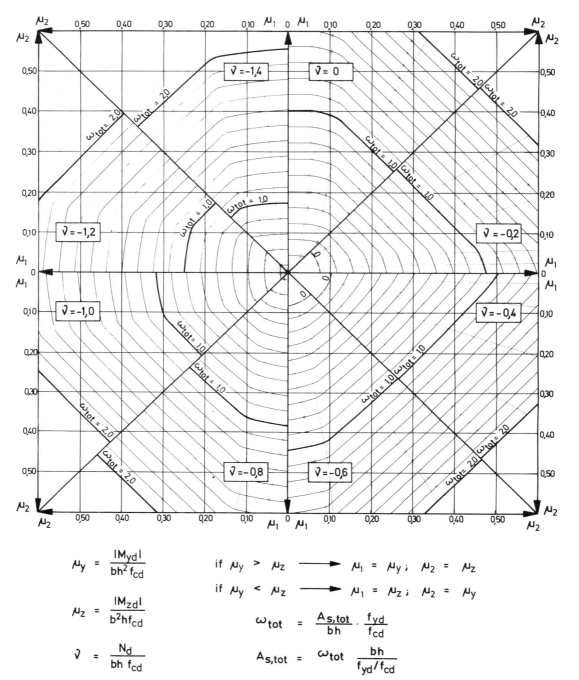

$$\mu_y = \frac{|M_{yd}|}{bh^2 f_{cd}} \qquad \text{if } \mu_y > \mu_z \longrightarrow \mu_1 = \mu_y \, ; \quad \mu_2 = \mu_z$$

$$\text{if } \mu_y < \mu_z \longrightarrow \mu_1 = \mu_z \, ; \quad \mu_2 = \mu_y$$

$$\mu_z = \frac{|M_{zd}|}{b^2 h f_{cd}} \qquad \omega_{tot} = \frac{A_{s,tot}}{bh} \cdot \frac{f_{yd}}{f_{cd}}$$

$$\nu = \frac{N_d}{bh \, f_{cd}} \qquad A_{s,tot} = \omega_{tot} \frac{bh}{f_{yd}/f_{cd}}$$

Reinforcement arrangement see section at head of the table

Design Chart 43   Enlargement of Design Chart 42

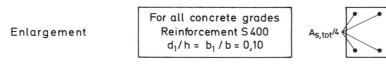

Enlargement

For all concrete grades
Reinforcement S 400
$d_1 / h = b_1 / b = 0{,}10$

$A_{s,tot}/4$

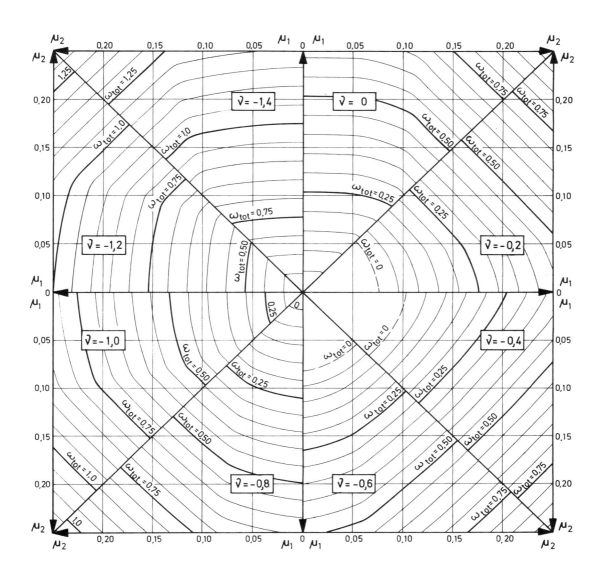

Design formulae see opposite page

73

Design Chart 44 Interaction diagram for a rectangular section under biaxial bending and axial force (S 400; reinforcement arrangement 2)

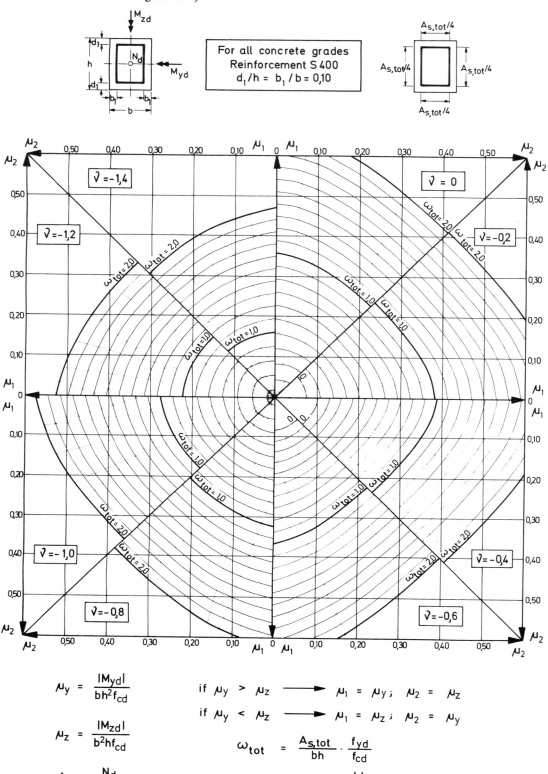

$$\mu_y = \frac{|M_{yd}|}{bh^2 f_{cd}}$$

if $\mu_y > \mu_z$ ⟶ $\mu_1 = \mu_y$; $\mu_2 = \mu_z$

if $\mu_y < \mu_z$ ⟶ $\mu_1 = \mu_z$; $\mu_2 = \mu_y$

$$\mu_z = \frac{|M_{zd}|}{b^2 h f_{cd}}$$

$$\omega_{tot} = \frac{A_{s,tot}}{bh} \cdot \frac{f_{yd}}{f_{cd}}$$

$$\cdot \nu = \frac{N_d}{bh\, f_{cd}}$$

$$A_{s,tot} = \omega_{tot}\,\frac{bh}{f_{yd}/f_{cd}}$$

Reinforcement arrangement see section at head of the table

Design Chart 45   Enlargement of Design Chart 44

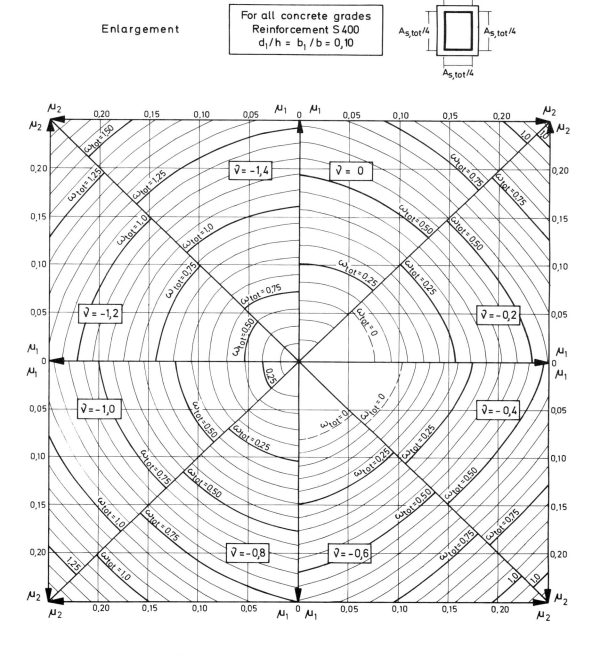

Design formulae see opposite page

Design Chart 46 Interaction diagram for a rectangular section under biaxial bending and axial force (S 400; reinforcement arrangement 3)

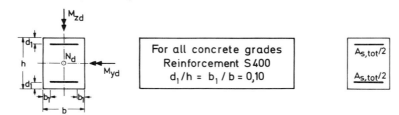

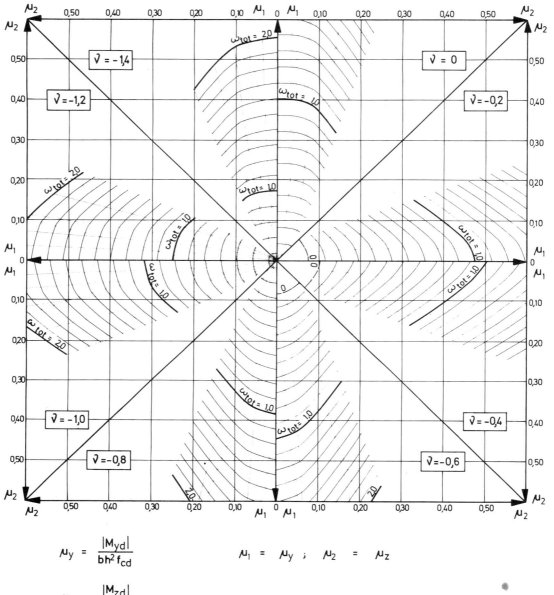

$$\mu_y = \frac{|M_{yd}|}{bh^2 f_{cd}}$$

$$\mu_1 = \mu_y \; ; \; \mu_2 = \mu_z$$

$$\mu_z = \frac{|M_{zd}|}{b^2 h f_{cd}}$$

$$\omega_{tot} = \frac{A_{s,tot}}{bh} \cdot \frac{f_{yd}}{f_{cd}}$$

$$\nu = \frac{N_d}{bh f_{cd}}$$

$$A_{s,tot} = \omega_{tot} \frac{bh}{f_{yd}/f_{cd}}$$

Reinforcement arrangement see section at head of the table

Design Chart 47   Enlargement of Design Chart 46

Enlargement

| For all concrete grades |
| Reinforcement S 400 |
| $d_1/h = b_1/b = 0,10$ |

$$\overline{A_{s,tot}/2}$$

$$\underline{A_{s,tot}/2}$$

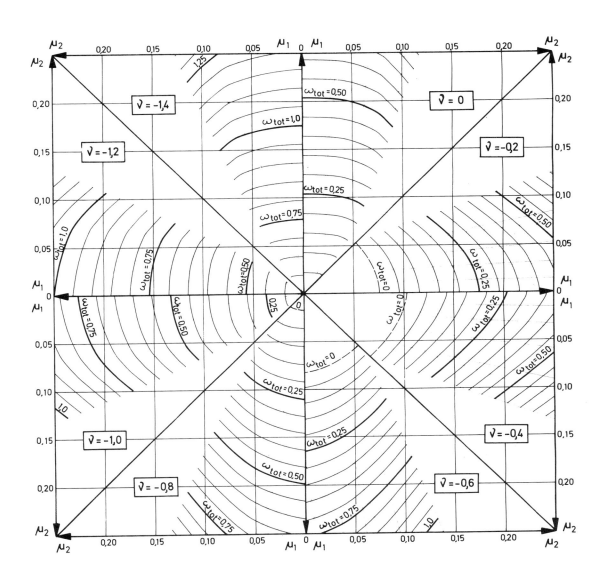

Design   formulae   see   opposite   page

Design Chart 48 Interaction diagram for a rectangular section under biaxial bending and axial force (S 400; reinforcement arrangement 4)

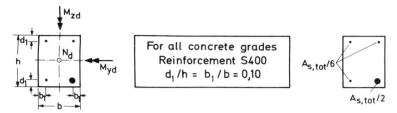

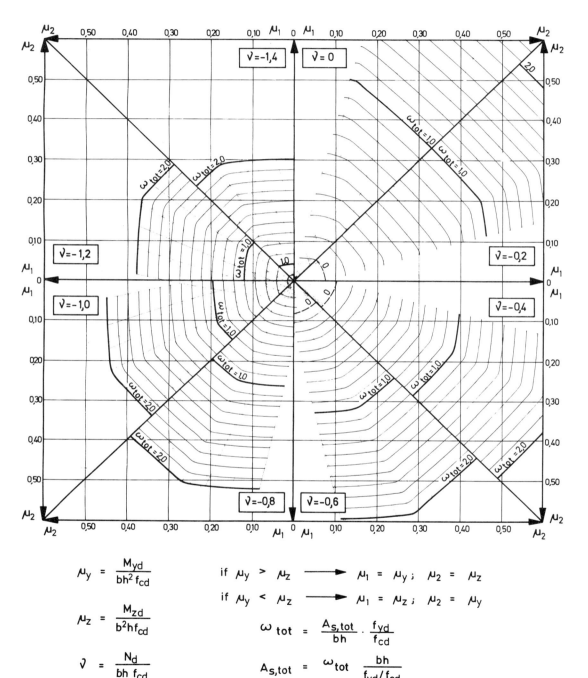

$$\mu_y = \frac{M_{yd}}{bh^2 f_{cd}}$$

if $\mu_y > \mu_z \longrightarrow \mu_1 = \mu_y ; \quad \mu_2 = \mu_z$

if $\mu_y < \mu_z \longrightarrow \mu_1 = \mu_z ; \quad \mu_2 = \mu_y$

$$\mu_z = \frac{M_{zd}}{b^2 h f_{cd}}$$

$$\omega_{tot} = \frac{A_{s,tot}}{bh} \cdot \frac{f_{yd}}{f_{cd}}$$

$$\nu = \frac{N_d}{bh f_{cd}}$$

$$A_{s,tot} = \omega_{tot} \frac{bh}{f_{yd}/f_{cd}}$$

Reinforcement arrangement see section at head of the table

Design Chart 49   Enlargement of Design Chart 48

Enlargement

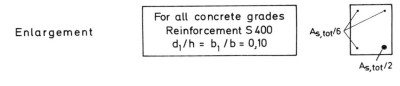

For all concrete grades
Reinforcement S 400
$d_1/h = b_1/b = 0,10$

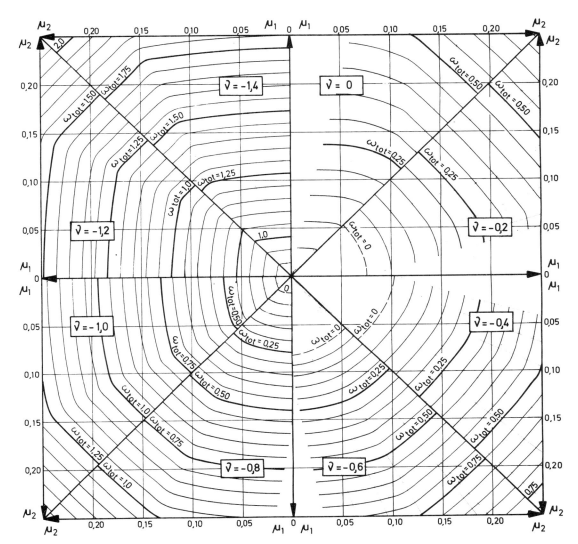

Design formulae see opposite page

Design Chart 50 Interaction diagram for a rectangular section under biaxial bending and axial force (S 500; reinforcement arrangement 1)

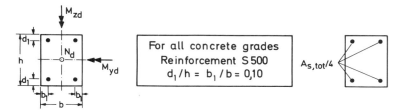

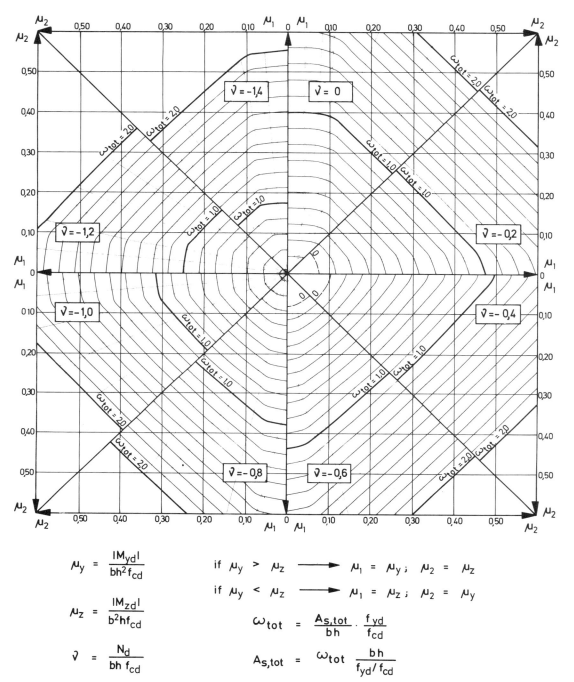

$$\mu_y = \frac{|M_{yd}|}{bh^2 f_{cd}}$$

$$\mu_z = \frac{|M_{zd}|}{b^2 h f_{cd}}$$

$$\nu = \frac{N_d}{bh f_{cd}}$$

if $\mu_y > \mu_z \longrightarrow \mu_1 = \mu_y;\quad \mu_2 = \mu_z$

if $\mu_y < \mu_z \longrightarrow \mu_1 = \mu_z;\quad \mu_2 = \mu_y$

$$\omega_{tot} = \frac{A_{s,tot}}{bh} \cdot \frac{f_{yd}}{f_{cd}}$$

$$A_{s,tot} = \omega_{tot} \frac{bh}{f_{yd}/f_{cd}}$$

Reinforcement arrangement see section at head of the table

Design Chart 51 Interaction diagram for a rectangular section under biaxial bending and axial force (S 500; reinforcement arrangement 2)

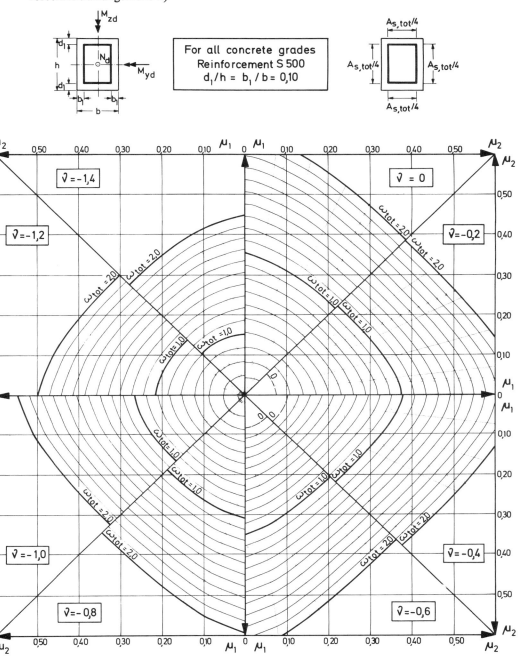

$$\mu_y = \frac{|M_{yd}|}{bh^2 f_{cd}}$$

if $\mu_y > \mu_z \longrightarrow \mu_1 = \mu_y ; \quad \mu_2 = \mu_z$

if $\mu_y < \mu_z \longrightarrow \mu_1 = \mu_z ; \quad \mu_2 = \mu_y$

$$\mu_z = \frac{|M_{zd}|}{b^2 h f_{cd}}$$

$$\omega_{tot} = \frac{A_{s,tot}}{bh} \cdot \frac{f_{yd}}{f_{cd}}$$

$$\vartheta = \frac{N_d}{bh\, f_{cd}}$$

$$A_{s,tot} = \omega_{tot} \frac{bh}{f_{yd}/f_{cd}}$$

Reinforcement arrangement see section at head of the table

Design Chart 52 **Interaction diagram for a rectangular section under biaxial bending and axial force (S 500; reinforcement arrangement 3)**

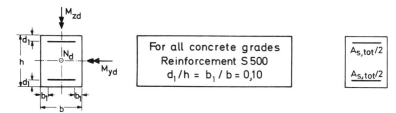

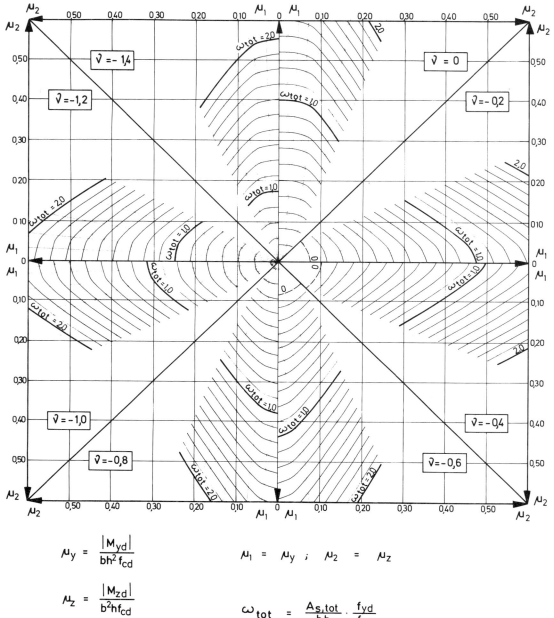

$$\mu_y = \frac{|M_{yd}|}{bh^2 f_{cd}}$$

$$\mu_1 = \mu_y \; ; \quad \mu_2 = \mu_z$$

$$\mu_z = \frac{|M_{zd}|}{b^2 h f_{cd}}$$

$$\omega_{tot} = \frac{A_{s,tot}}{bh} \cdot \frac{f_{yd}}{f_{cd}}$$

$$\nu = \frac{N_d}{bh f_{cd}}$$

$$A_{s,tot} = \omega_{tot} \frac{bh}{f_{yd}/f_{cd}}$$

Reinforcement arrangement see section at head of the table

Design Chart 53 **Interaction diagram for a rectangular section under biaxial bending and axial force (S 500; reinforcement arrangement 4)**

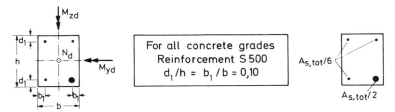

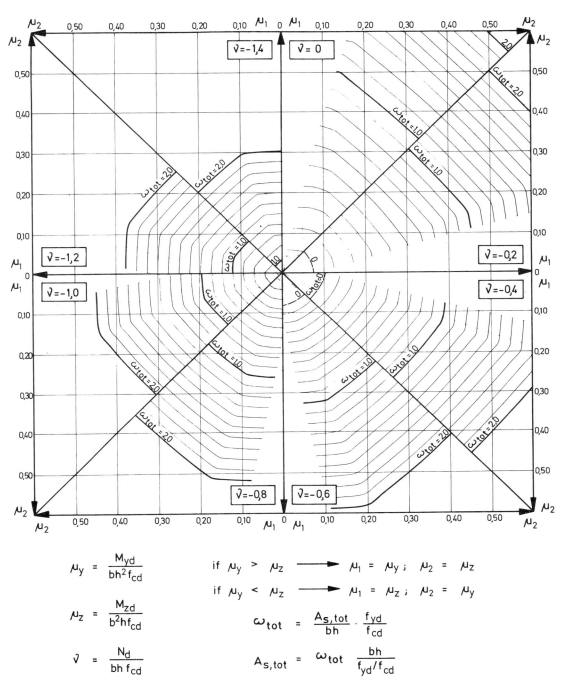

$$\mu_y = \frac{M_{yd}}{bh^2 f_{cd}}$$

if $\mu_y > \mu_z \longrightarrow \mu_1 = \mu_y ; \quad \mu_2 = \mu_z$

if $\mu_y < \mu_z \longrightarrow \mu_1 = \mu_z ; \quad \mu_2 = \mu_y$

$$\mu_z = \frac{M_{zd}}{b^2 h f_{cd}}$$

$$\omega_{tot} = \frac{A_{s,tot}}{bh} \cdot \frac{f_{yd}}{f_{cd}}$$

$$\nu = \frac{N_d}{bh f_{cd}}$$

$$A_{s,tot} = \omega_{tot} \frac{bh}{f_{yd}/f_{cd}}$$

Reinforcement arrangement see section at head of the table

Example 16

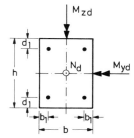

b = 0.30 m	γ_s = 1.15	f_{yk} = 400 MPa
h = 0.40 m	γ_c = 1.50	f_{ck} = 20 MPa
b_1 = 0.03 m		
d_1 = 0.04 m		

N_d = −810 kN M_{yd} = 87 kNm M_{zd} = 43.5 kNm

f_{yd} = 400/1.15 = 348 MPa

f_{cd} = 20/1.5 = 13.3 MPa

$$\nu = \frac{-810 \cdot 10^{-3}}{0.3 \cdot 0.4 \cdot 13.3} = -0.51$$

$$\mu_y = \frac{87 \cdot 10^{-3}}{0.3 \cdot 0.4^2 \cdot 13.3} = 0.136_5$$

$$\mu_z = \frac{43.5 \cdot 10^{-3}}{0.3^2 \cdot 0.4 \cdot 13.3} = 0.091$$

From Design Chart 42 or 43 (Enlargement) we obtain:

if $\mu_y > \mu_z$: $\mu_1 = \mu_y = 0.136$

$\mu_2 = \mu_z = 0.091$

for $\nu = -0.40$: $\omega_{tot} = 0.25$

for $\nu = -0.60$: $\omega_{tot} = 0.31$

by interpolation

for $\nu = -0.51$ $\omega_{tot} = 0.28$

$$A_{s,\,tot} = 0.28\,\frac{30 \cdot 40}{348/13.3} = 12.8 \text{ cm}^2$$

3.5.2 Approximate formulae for symmetrical reinforcement

Scope An approximate method is given for dimensioning rectangular cross-sections subjected to biaxial bending. The total amount of reinforcement along each side must be the same.

The biaxial bending problem is reduced to an equivalent uniaxial bending problem. The axial force is the same, acting with a fictitious eccentricity e'_z which is obtained as a function of the eccentricities e_y, e_z and of the reduced axial force ν (see Fig. 3.9).

Figure 3.9 Real and fictitious eccentricities of the normal force

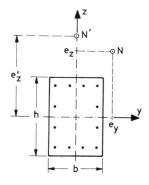

Use   Compute the fictitious eccentricity e_z':

$$e_z' = e_z + \beta \, e_y \cdot \frac{h}{b} \qquad (3.58)$$

with:

β = coefficient given in Fig. 3.10 as a function of the reduced axial force

$e_z = M_{yd}/N_d$

$e_y = M_{zd}/N_d$

h, b   dimensions in the z- and y-direction

Note that $e_z/e_y \geqslant h/b$, otherwise the y- and z-coordinates must be exchanged.

The resulting uniaxial bending problem (a reduced axial force ν acting with the eccentricity e_z') is solved by any of the procedures used for prevailing bending or compression in the plane of symmetry (see 3.2 or 3.3).

If the resulting mechanical percentage, ω, is greater than 0.60 it is necessary to try a different design with the value β increased by 0.1. On the other hand, for a resulting ω lower than 0.20, a decrease of 0.1 in the value of β is possible.

Figure 3.10   Coefficient β as a function of the reduced normal force ν

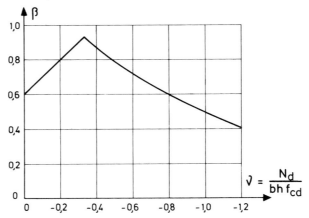

Example 17

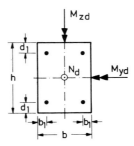

b   = 0.30 m γ_s = 1.15 f_{yk} = 400 MPa

h   = 0.40 m γ_c = 1.50 f_{ck} =   20 MPa

d_1 = 0.04 m

N_d = −810 kN M_{yd} = 87 kNm M_{zd} = 43.5 kNm

f_{yd} = 400/1.15 = 348 MPa

f_{cd} = 20/1.15 = 13.3 MPa

$$e_z = \frac{M_{yd}}{N_d} = 0.107 \text{ m}$$

$$e_y = \frac{M_{zd}}{N_d} = 0.054 \text{ m}$$

$$\frac{e_z}{e_y} = \frac{0.107}{0.054} = 1.98 \geqslant \frac{h}{b} = 1.33$$

$$\nu = \frac{N_d}{b\,h\,f_{cd}} = -0.51$$

From Fig. 3.10 we obtain: $\beta = 0.78$

$$e_z' = 0.107 + 0.78 \cdot 0.054 \cdot \frac{0.4}{0.3} = 0.163 \text{ m}$$

The design will be performed with symmetrical reinforcement (see 3.3.1.1).

$$\mu = \frac{-810 \cdot 0.163}{0.3 \cdot 0.4^2 \cdot 13.3} = 0.207$$

$$\nu = -0.51$$

From Design Chart 16 we obtain: $\omega_{tot} = 0.31$

$$A_{s,\,tot} = 0.31 \frac{30 \cdot 40}{348/13.3} = 14.2 \text{ cm}^2$$

3.6 SPECIAL PROBLEMS

3.6.1 Application of the rectangular stress block

Scope In general the design of reinforced concrete cross-sections can be carried out very simply with the help of graphs, tables or formulae derived using the parabolic—rectangular stress-distribution in the compression zone. But there remain some problems of dimensioning special types of cross-sections for which no charts, tables or formulae are available. In such cases, if a computer program cannot be used, the design must be done by hand, solving the equilibrium equations for the cross-section by iteration. In these cases, the application of the parabolic—rectangular stress-distribution leads to time consuming integrations and it is recommended that the rectangular stress-distribution be used (see 2.3.3 of this manual).

An arbitrary cross-section may be acted upon by a combination of a normal force N_{Sd} at the centroid of the cross-section and moments M_{Syd} and M_{Szd} acting in the directions of a coordinate system at the centroid (see Fig. 3.11). It must be shown that these internal forces can be resisted at the ultimate limit state by the section. In general, it must be shown that there exists a stress state where the resisting action-effects exceed the acting design action effects and the line connecting the centroids of tensile and compressive stresses is perpendicular to the resulting moment vector M_{Sd} (see Fig. 3.11). That means that the eccentric acting normal force must also be on this line.

Figure 3.11   External loading and assumed internal stress and strain state of an arbitrary cross-section at the ultimate limit state

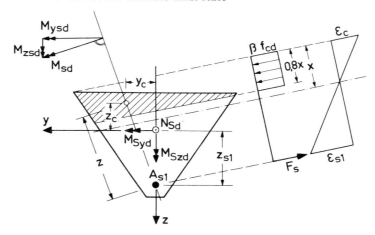

Use First, the position of the neutral axis must be chosen. Then the compressed concrete area A_{cc} is determined as the concrete area having a distance of more than 0.2 x from the neutral axis. Its centroid has the coordinates y_c and z_c. The strain diagram is defined in accordance with the possible strain diagrams for the ultimate limit state given in Fig. 10.1 of the Model Code. From the strain diagram, the strain ϵ_{si} for any steel bar i can be determined and hence the stress σ_{si}. If each bar has the area A_{si} and the coordinates are y_{si} and z_{si} the resisting internal forces are:

$$N_{Rd} = \Sigma A_{si}\, \sigma_{si} - \beta \cdot f_{cd}\, A_{cc} \tag{3.59}$$

$$M_{Ryd} = \Sigma A_{si}\, \sigma_{si}\, z_{si} - \beta \cdot f_{cd}\, A_{cc}\, z_c \tag{3.60}$$

$$M_{Rzd} = \Sigma A_{si}\, \sigma_{si}\, y_{si} + \beta \cdot f_{cd}\, A_{cc}\, y_c \tag{3.61}$$

where $\beta = 0.85$ if the width of the compression zone increases towards the extreme fibre in compression and $\beta = 0.80$ if it decreases.

If there is a distinct centroid of the tension force with coordinates y_s and z_s and a centroid of the compression force with coordinates y_c and z_c, the design procedure can be simplified using the resulting moment M_{sd} with respect to the tension reinforcement

$$M_{sd} = \sqrt{M_{ysd}^2 + M_{zsd}^2} \tag{3.62}$$

with:

$$M_{ysd} = M_{Syd} - N_{Sd} \cdot z_s \tag{3.63}$$

$$M_{zsd} = M_{Szd} + N_{Sd} \cdot y_s \tag{3.64}$$

The direction of M_{sd} must be perpendicular to the line connecting the centroids of the compression and tension forces (see Fig. 3.11).

From the equilibrium of normal forces the required amount of reinforcement, A_s, is given by:

$$A_s = \frac{1}{\sigma_{sd}} \left(\frac{M_{sd}}{z} + N \right) \tag{3.65}$$

where the design steel stress σ_{sd} will normally be equal to the design strength f_{yd} and z is the lever arm of the internal forces

$$z = \sqrt{(y_s - y_c)^2 + (z_s - z_c)^2} \tag{3.66}$$

The iteration is finished if the eccentricity e_S of the acting forces

$$e_S = \frac{M_{sd}}{N_{sd}} \tag{3.67a}$$

is smaller than or equal to the eccentricity e_R of the resulting resistant internal force

$$e_R = \frac{F_c \cdot z}{F_c - F_s} \tag{3.67b}$$

with

$$F_c = \beta f_{cd}\, A_{cc}$$

$$F_s = \sigma_{sd} \cdot A_s$$

Example 18 – T-beam in biaxial bending

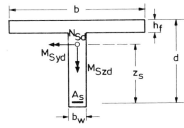

b $= 1.50\,\text{m}$	$\gamma_s = 1.15$	$f_{yk} = 400\,\text{MPa}$
$b_w = 0.20\,\text{m}$	$\gamma_c = 1.50$	$f_{ck} = 40\,\text{MPa}$
d $= 0.95\,\text{m}$	$f_{yd} = 400/1.15 = 348\,\text{MPa}$	
$h_f = 0.15\,\text{m}$	$f_{cd} = 40/1.50 = 26.7\,\text{MPa}$	
$z_s = 0.66\,\text{m}$		

$$N_{Sd} = -1500 \text{ kN} \qquad M_{Syd} = 2030 \text{ kNm} \qquad M_{Szd} = 750 \text{ kNm}$$

In the following, only the final step of the iteration is demonstrated (see Fig. 3.12)

$$A_{cc} = 0.163 \text{ m}^2 \qquad y_c = 0.22 \text{ m} \qquad z_c = -0.22 \text{ m}$$
$$A_s = 55 \text{ cm}^2 \qquad y_s = 0 \qquad z_s = 0.66 \text{ m}$$
$$\epsilon_c = -3.5‰$$
$$\epsilon_s = 3.0‰ \qquad \sigma_s = f_{yd} = 34.8 \text{ kN/cm}^2$$

$\beta = 0.80$ since the width of the compression zone decreases towards the extreme fibre in compression.

$$N_{Rd} = 55 \cdot 34.8 - 0.8 \cdot 26.7 \cdot 0.163 \cdot 10^3$$
$$= 1914 - 3482 = -1570 \text{ kN} \cong N_{Sd} = -1500 \text{ kN}$$

$$M_{Ryd} = 1914 \cdot 0.66 + 3482 \cdot 0.22 = 2029 \text{ kNm} \cong M_{Syd}$$

$$M_{Rzd} = 1914 \cdot 0 + 3482 \cdot 0.22 = 766 \text{ kNm} \cong M_{Szd} = 750 \text{ kNm}$$

Using the simplified method the procedure is as follows

$$M_{ysd} = 2030 + 1500 \cdot 0.66 = 3020 \text{ kNm}$$

$$M_{zsd} = 750 \text{ kNm}$$

$$M_{sd} = \sqrt{3020^2 + 750^2} = 3110 \text{ kNm}$$

$$z = \sqrt{(0 - 0.22)^2 + (0.66 + 0.22)^2} = 0.91 \text{ m}$$

$$A_s = \frac{1}{34.8} \frac{3110}{0.91} - 1500 = 55 \text{ cm}^2$$

$$F_c = 0.80 \cdot 26.7 \cdot 0.163 \cdot 10^3 = 3482 \text{ kN}$$

$$F_s = 34.8 \cdot 55 = 1914 \text{ kN}$$

$$e_S = \frac{3110}{1500} = 2.07 \text{ m} \cong e_R = \frac{3482 \cdot 0.91}{3482 - 1914} = 2.02 \text{ m}$$

Figure 3.12 Internal stress and strain state assumed for Example 18

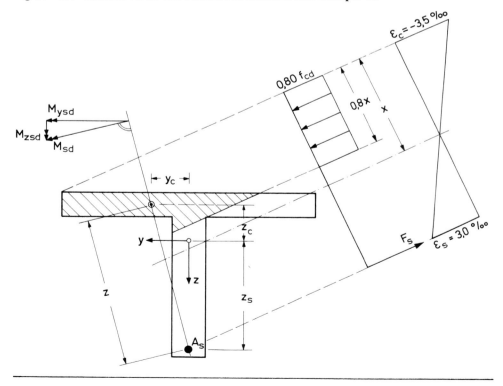

3.6.2 Influence of prestress

3.6.2.1 Survey

Regulations for the treatment of prestressing in design are given in §4 of the Model Code. Prestresssing of the tendons can be done either before placing of the concrete (pretensioning) or after hardening of of the concrete (post-tensioning). In general the Model Code covers only the case of tendons held in internal sheaths acting compositely with the concrete by means of grouting. It does not deal with the case of tendons placed outside a member.

Representative values of the prestressing force can be calculated taking into account the losses due to:

— friction in the sheaths
— slip in the anchoring devices
— relaxation of the prestressing steel
— immediate deformations of concrete
— creep and shrinkage of concrete.

For most cases it is sufficient to take account of the values of prestress

— at the instant of the application of the prestress to the concrete (t = 0)
— at long term (t = ∞).

For the most commonly encountered cases the mean value of expected prestress can be taken into consideration for design and calculated from

$$P_{mt}(x) = P_o - [\Delta P_o(x) + \Delta P_t(x)] \qquad (3.68)$$

with:

$P_{mt}(x)$ = mean value of prestress at time t and section x

P_o = initial prestress (t = 0) at the origin (x = 0)

$\Delta P_o(x)$ = losses before and during prestressing of the concrete at section x

$\Delta P_t(x)$ = time dependent losses at section x.

The isostatic effects of the prestress are taken into account for design

— as an element of the resisting load effects for tendons subjected to an elongation which is not less than ϵ_{pk} corresponding to the stress $f_{p\,0.1\,k}$,

— as an element of the applied load effect where the elongation of the tendons does not exceed ϵ_{pk}.

The hyperstatic effects are always taken into account as an element of the applied load effect.

3.6.2.2 Design procedure

Scope The design procedure given in the following is applicable to sections prestressed by bonded tendons if the effect of prestressing can be taken into account as an element of the resisting load effect (see §4.5.2 of the Model Code). Design aids are provided for T-beam sections and rectangular sections as a limiting case. It is assumed that the design action-effects have already been determined.

Use The section is acted upon by a normal force N_d at the centroid and a bending moment M_d. The bending moment M_{pd} with respect to the axis of the prestressed reinforcement is

$$M_{pd} = M_d - N_d \cdot y_p \qquad (3.69)$$

with y_p = distance between axis of prestressed steel and neutral axis (see Fig. 3.13).

This bending moment is reduced to the non-dimensional value

$$\mu_{pd} = \frac{M_{pd}}{b\,d_p^2\,f_{cd}}$$

Entering the diagram in Fig. 3.14 with μ_{pd} and the geometrical parameters b_e/b_w and h_f/d of the cross-section, the lever arm $z = \zeta \cdot d_p$ of internal forces and the strain $\Delta\epsilon_p$ can be obtained. $\Delta\epsilon_p$ is the strain of the concrete fibre adjacent to the prestressed reinforcement at the ultimate limit state (see Fig. 10.1 of the Model Code). To get the total strain ϵ_p in the prestressed reinforcement, the preliminary elongation ϵ_{pt} due to prestressing must be added (see Fig. 3.13).

Figure 3.13   Strain state at the ultimate limit state of a prestressed concrete beam

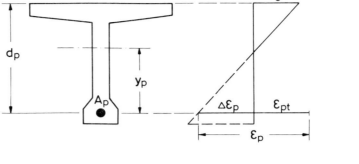

$$\epsilon_p = \epsilon_{pt} + \Delta\epsilon_p \qquad (3.71)$$

For the determination of ϵ_{pt}, losses of the prestressing force due to creep and shrinkage must be taken into account.

In the case of prestressing by post-tensioning, the preliminary elongation ϵ_{pt} can be calculated as the difference between steel strain and the strain of the adjacent concrete fibre due to the prestressing force

$$\epsilon_{pt} = \frac{P_{mt}(x)}{A_p E_p} - \frac{\sigma_{cp}}{E_c} \qquad (3.72)$$

with:

$P_{mt}(x)$ = mean value of prestressing force with losses taken into account (eq (3.68))

A_p = cross-sectional area of prestressed steel

Figure 3.14   Lever arm and reinforcement strain at the ultimate limit state as a function of the reduced bending moment μ_{pd}

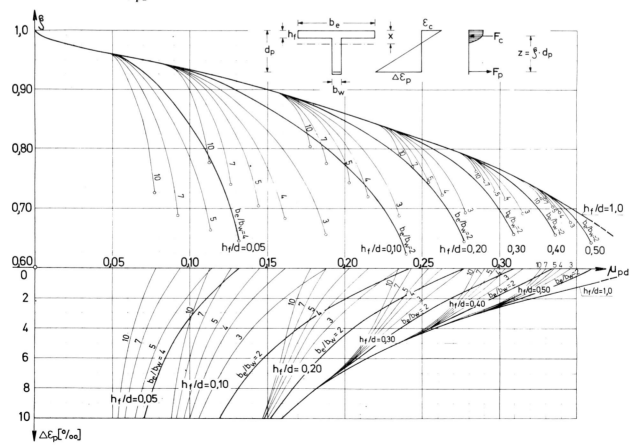

E_p, E_c = elastic moduli of prestressing steel and concrete

$$\sigma_{cp} = -\frac{P_{mt}(x)}{A_c} - \frac{P_{mt}(x) \cdot y_p^2}{I_c} \qquad (3.73)$$

A_c = cross-sectional area of concrete

I_c = moment of inertia of concrete.

In the case of prestressing by pretensioning, the preliminary elongation ϵ_{pt} can be determined from the stress σ_{pto} in the prestressed steel when the concrete fibre adjacent to the prestressing steel is unstressed

$$\epsilon_{pt} = \frac{\sigma_{pto}}{E_p} \qquad (3.74)$$

From the design stress–strain relationship of the particular prestressing steel used, the design stress σ_{pd} is obtained as a function of ϵ_p. The necessary amount of prestressed reinforcement is calculated from

$$A_p = \frac{1}{\sigma_{pd}}\left(\frac{M_{pd}}{z} + N_d\right) \qquad (3.75)$$

with:

N_d = design normal force acting at the centroid of the section

M_{pd} = from equation (3.69)

z = lever arm obtained from Fig. 3.14.

If an amount of non-prestressed reinforcement is used which carries a significant part of the applied moment the contribution of the stresses in the non-prestressed reinforcement to M_{pd} must be considered.

Example 19

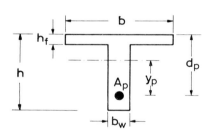

b = 3.00 m	d_p = 1.75 m	f_{ck} = 50 MPa
b_w = 0.60 m	y_p = 0.98 m	γ_c = 1.50
h_f = 0.30 m		
h = 2.20 m		
A_c = 2.04 m²	I_c = 0.95 m⁴	
Prestressing steel:	A_p = 135 cm²	

The design stress–strain relationship is shown in Fig. 3.15. The representative value of the prestressing force is:

$$P_{mf}(x) = 7.86 \text{ MN}$$

The design load effects have been determined as:

$$M_d = 30 \text{ MNm} \qquad N_d = -7 \text{ MN}$$

$$M_{pd} = 30 + 7 \cdot 0.98 = 36.9 \text{ MNm}$$

To enter the diagram in Fig. 3.14 we need:

$$\mu_{pd} = \frac{36.9}{3.0 \cdot 1.75^2 \cdot 50/1.50} = 0.12$$

$$h_f/d_p = 0.30/1.75 = 0.17$$

$$b/b_w = 3.0/0.6 = 5$$

Figure 3.15 **Characteristic and design stress–strain curves of the prestressing steel of Example 19**

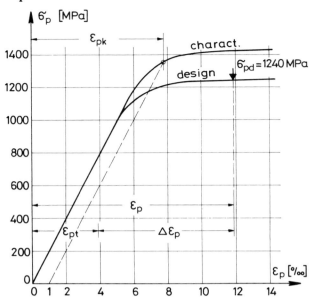

The value for $\Delta\epsilon_p$ and ζ are found by interpolation

$$h_f/d = 0.10 \qquad \Delta\epsilon_p = 3.4\text{‰}; \qquad \zeta = 0.86$$
$$h_f/d = 0.20 \qquad \Delta\epsilon_p = 10.0\text{‰}; \qquad \zeta = 0.92$$
$$h_f/d = 0.17 \qquad \Delta\epsilon_p = 8.0\text{‰}; \qquad \zeta = 0.90$$

$$z = \zeta \cdot d_p = 0.90 \cdot 1.75 = 1.58 \text{ m}$$

$$\sigma_{cp} = -\frac{7.86}{2.04} - \frac{7.86 \cdot 0.98^2}{0.95} = -11.8 \text{ MN/m}^2$$

$$\epsilon_{pt} = \frac{7.86}{135 \cdot 10^{-4} \cdot 2.0 \cdot 10^5} + \frac{11.8}{37000} = 3.93\text{‰}$$

$$\epsilon_p = 3.93 + 8.0 = 11.93\text{‰}$$

From the design stress curve of the prestressing steel (Fig. 3.15):

$$\sigma_{pd} = 1240 \text{ MPa}$$

$$A_p = \frac{1}{1240}\left(\frac{36.9}{1.58} - 7.0\right)10^4 = 132 \text{ cm}^2 < 135 \text{ cm}^2$$

Appendix 1.
Effective width of T-beams

A1.1 GENERAL

In a T-beam the normal stresses acting parallel to the beam axis in the flange caused by bending moments are not constant over the width of the flange but decrease away from the web. For simplification it is convenient to adopt a uniform distribution of stress over a reduced width of the flange, called the effective width b_{ef}. The magnitude of the effective width is defined by the conditions that the assumed uniform stress is equal to the peak stress of the real stress distribution and that the resulting normal force is equal for both stress distributions (see Fig. A1.1). For the determination of the effective width it is assumed that the material behaves elastically and that there are end diaphragms which are infinitely rigid for displacements in their plane and infinitely non-rigid for displacements in the direction perpendicular to this plane.

Figure A1.1 The effective width of a T-beam section

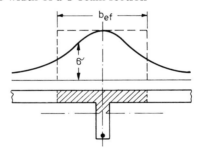

Using effective width, idealized cross-sections of the T-beams are defined. These can be used for the analysis of structures (Model Code §8.6) or for the design of T-beam-sections at the ultimate limit state (Model Code §10.3). The determination of the effective width using the theory of elasticity yields results which are on the safe side for design. If the non-linear behaviour of concrete is taken into account, the effective width would be larger.

The magnitude of the effective width is influenced by the web and flange dimensions, by the type of loading, by the length of span and by the support conditions of the beam.

A1.2 DETERMINATION OF THE EFFECTIVE WIDTH

A1.2.1 Approximate method of the Model Code

A rough estimation of the effective width is given by (Model Code §8.6):

$$b_{ef} = b_w + \frac{1}{5} \ell_0 \leqslant b \qquad (A1.1)$$

with:

b_{ef} = effective width

b_w = web thickness

ℓ_0 = distance between points of zero moment

b = total width of the beam

This appendix is based on a proposal by S Schröder, Dresden.

In accordance with §7.2.1.1 (left side) of the Model Code, the distance ℓ_0 between points of zero moment can be approximated by

$$\ell_0 = \alpha \cdot \ell \tag{A1.2}$$

with α being a coefficient tabulated in Table 16.1 of the Model Code and ℓ being the effective span. The values for α can be taken for the span regions

of simply supported beams as $\qquad \alpha = 1.0$
of the end span of continuous beams as $\qquad \alpha = 0.8$
of interior spans of continuous beams as $\qquad \alpha = 0.6$

For the determination of the effective width for cantilever beams the α value of Table 16.1 of the Model Code ($\alpha = 2.4$) should be substituted by $\alpha = 1.5$. The approximations for ℓ_0 are summarised in Fig. A1.2.

The effective width calculated from equation (A1.1) can be taken as constant over the entire span, including the parts near intermediate supports for continuous beams.

Figure A1.2   Approximations for the distance ℓ_0 between points of zero moment

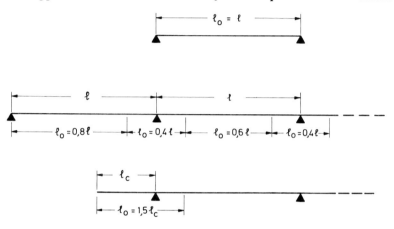

A1.2.2   Refined method   A more precise value of the effective width b_{ef} can be calculated from equations (A1.2) to (A1.5).

$$b_{ef} = b_w + b_{ef,\,1} + b_{ef,\,2} \leqslant b \tag{A1.3}$$

The values of $b_{ef,\,i}$ (i = 1 or 2; see also Fig. A1.3) depend on the type of loading. In the vicinity of concentrated loads they are reduced. For the determination of the effective width, it is usually sufficient to consider only two cases. If the moment diagram is parabolic, which can usually be assumed for span regions provided concentrated loads do not dominate

$$b_{ef,\,i} = \beta_1 \cdot b_i \tag{A1.4}$$

and if the moment diagram is triangular which can usually be assumed in the support regions of continuous beams

$$b_{ef,\,i} = \beta_2 \cdot b_i \tag{A1.5}$$

Figure A1.3   Definition of dimensions

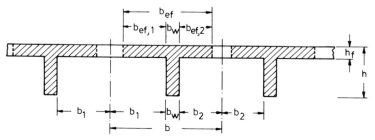

The dimensions $b_{ef,i}$ and b_i ($i = 1$ or 2) are shown in Fig. A1.3. The coefficients β_1 and β_2 are tabulated in Tables A1.1 and A1.2 as a function of b_i/ℓ_0 and h_f/h. For the distance ℓ_0 between points of zero moment the approximations described in A1.2.1 can be used.

Table A1.1 Values $\beta_1 = b_{ef,i}/b_i$ for parabolic moment diagram

h_f/h	b_i/ℓ_0								
	1.0	*0.8*	*0.6*	*0.5*	*0.4*	*0.3*	*0.2*	*0.1*	*0.05*
$\leqslant 0.15$	0.20	0.25	0.33	0.40	0.49	0.62	0.78	0.94	1.00
0.20	0.22	0.27	0.35	0.42	0.52	0.64	0.78	0.94	1.00
0.30	0.33	0.40	0.50	0.56	0.63	0.72	0.83	0.94	1.00

Table A1.2 Values $\beta_2 = b_{ef,i}/b_i$ for triangular moment diagram

h_f/h	b_i/ℓ_0								
	1.0	*0.8*	*0.6*	*0.5*	*0.4*	*0.3*	*0.2*	*0.1*	*0.05*
$\leqslant 0.15$	0.12	0.14	0.19	0.23	0.30	0.38	0.50	0.74	0.97
0.20	0.13	0.15	0.20	0.25	0.30	0.38	0.50	0.74	0.97
0.30	0.22	0.25	0.31	0.36	0.40	0.47	0.57	0.74	0.97

If in special cases the effective width is to be calculated for spans of constant bending moment, values $\beta_3 = b_{ef,i}/b_i$ of Table A1.4 can be used.

If the effective width is to be calculated in the support regions of a continous beam with a bottom flange which is acting in compression due to negative moments, the value β_2 should be determined with

$$\ell_0 = 0.4\,\ell \qquad\qquad (A1.6)$$

The approximations for ℓ_0 are summarized in Fig. A1.2.

If the determination of the effective width leads to a significantly asymmetric cross-section, torsion effects should be taken into account.

Table A1.3 Variation of the effective width along the beam axis

System		*Variation of effective width*
Simply supported beam		$\beta_2 \quad \beta_1 \quad \beta_2$
Continuous beam	End span	$\beta_2 \quad \beta_1 \quad \beta_2$
	Interior span	$\beta_2 \quad \beta_1 \quad \beta_2$
Cantilever beam		$\beta_1 \quad \beta_2$
$\ell_1 = b$, but not greater than $0.25\,\ell_j$ $\ell_2 = 0.1\ell$		

For the analysis of normal structures, especially for dwellings, office buildings, etc., it is sufficient to assume a constant effective width equal to the value in the middle of the span. For structures which need a more precise analysis, such as bridges, etc., the variation of the effective width along the axis can be taken in accordance with the simplified shape given in Table A1.3.

A1.3 EFFECTIVE WIDTH FOR NORMAL FORCES

For the determination of the effective width the regulations of §7.2.4.1 of the Model Code can be applied. According to this, a concentrated normal force is dispersed uniformly at an angle of 2β where $\tan \beta = 2/3$ (with $\beta \approx 34°$). It can be assumed that the dispersion starts at the point where the normal force is applied.

More precise results for the effective width $b_{ef,i}$ can be obtained from

$$b_{ef,i} = \beta_3 \cdot b_i \leqslant b \qquad (A1.7)$$

The coefficients β_3 are tabulated in Table A1.4 as a function of b_i/ℓ_0. In the case of normal forces, the distance between the points of application of the normal forces must be taken for ℓ_0.

The values β_3 can also be used to determine the effective width due to a constant moment diagram.

Table A1.4 Values $\beta_3 = b_{ef,i}/b_i$ for normal forces or for constant moment diagram

h_f/h	b_i/ℓ_0								
	1.0	*0.8*	*0.6*	*0.5*	*0.4*	*0.3*	*0.2*	*0.1*	*0.05*
$\leqslant 0.15$	0.26	0.32	0.45	0.55	0.67	0.83	0.95	1.00	1.00
0.20	0.32	0.37	0.50	0.60	0.71	0.87	0.95	1.00	1.00
0.30	0.51	0.57	0.70	0.78	0.87	0.91	0.95	1.00	1.00

Appendix 2.
Plane elements with reinforcement direction deviating from the direction of principal stresses

A2.1 GENERAL

The design procedure presented in the following satisfies equilibrium and compatibility conditions. It is based on linear elastic material behaviour. Concrete is assumed to have no tensile strength. Concrete compressive strains could, in general, be taken into account for compatibility but in the following they are neglected in favour of a simpler design procedure.

A plane reinforced concrete element is considered to be acted upon by membrane (in-plane) forces. It is assumed that these forces are carried by tensile stresses in a net of reinforcement bars in two or three directions and by concrete compressive stresses (struts).

All acting and resisting forces are given per unit length of the element. In the principal directions, only the principal normal forces n_1 and n_2 are acting. If they are both compressive forces, no reinforcement is necessary.

In slabs, the tension and the compression zone can be treated approximately as separate elements.

The requirement of the Model Code (§18.1.2.2.1) that the area of the secondary reinforcement be at least 20% of the area of the main reinforcement is not incorporated in the design procedure.

A2.2 DESIGN PROCEDURE FOR ELEMENTS WITH ORTHOGONAL REINFORCEMENT

Scope   The design procedure is applicable to plane reinforced concrete elements with orthogonal reinforcement under any combination of membrane forces. It can also be applied to the tension zone of reinforced concrete slabs.

Use   In the most general case, a slab element is acted upon by design moments m_ξ, m_η and $m_{\xi\eta}$ per unit length in a reference ξ-η-coordinate system. To obtain the corresponding membrane forces for the tension and compression zone, these moments are divided by the mean lever arm z_m of the internal forces (see Fig. A2.1)

$$n_{\xi,t} \ = \ \frac{m_\eta}{z_m} \ = \ -n_{\xi,c} \tag{A2.1a}$$

$$n_{\eta,t} \ = \ \frac{m_\xi}{z_m} \ = \ -n_{\eta,c} \tag{A2.1b}$$

$$n_{\xi\eta,t} = \ \frac{m_{\xi\eta}}{z_m} \ = \ -n_{\xi\eta,c} \tag{A2.1c}$$

$$z_m \ \ = \ (0.8 \div 0.9)\,\frac{d_x + d_y}{2} \tag{A2.2}$$

with:

$n_{\xi,t}$; $n_{\eta,t}$; $n_{\xi\eta,t}$ = membrane forces of the tension zone

$n_{\xi,c}$; $n_{\eta,c}$; $n_{\xi\eta,c}$ = membrane forces of the compression zone

d_x, d_y = effective height in the x and y direction

This appendix is based on a proposal of Th Baumann, München.

Figure A2.1   Slab element with orthogonal reinforcement in directions x and y under general loading

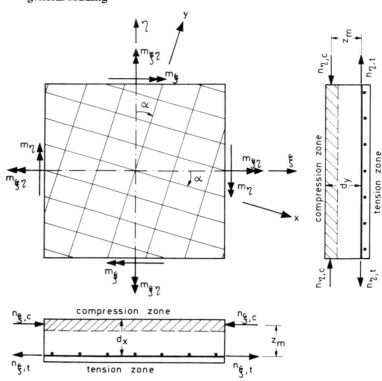

The membrane forces acting in the directions x and y of the reinforcement must be calculated from the forces in the directions ξ and η (eq (A2.3) to A2.5)) which are inclined at an angle α to the reinforcement direction (Fig. A2.1). This conversion can be omitted if the x, y and ξ, η coordinates coincide ($\alpha = 0$).

Table A2.1   Design formulae for elements with orthogonal reinforcement

Line	Condition	Tension force per unit length in reinforcement t_x	Tension force per unit length in reinforcement t_y	Compression force c_c per unit length in concrete
1	$n_x \geqslant -\lvert n_{xy}\rvert$ $n_y \geqslant -\lvert n_{xy}\rvert$	$n_x + \lvert n_{xy}\rvert$	$n_y + \lvert n_{xy}\rvert$	$-2\,\lvert n_{xy}\rvert$
2	$n_x < -\lvert n_{xy}\rvert$ $n_y > \dfrac{n_{xy}^2}{n_x} > -\lvert n_{xy}\rvert$	0	$n_y - \dfrac{n_{xy}^2}{n_x}$	$n_x + \dfrac{n_{xy}^2}{n_x}$
3	$n_x > \dfrac{n_{xy}^2}{n_y} > -\lvert n_{xy}\rvert$ $n_y < -\lvert n_{xy}\rvert$	$n_x - \dfrac{n_{xy}^2}{n_y}$	0	$n_y + \dfrac{n_{xy}^2}{n_y}$
4	$n_x < -\lvert n_{xy}\rvert$ $n_y < \dfrac{n_{xy}^2}{n_x}$	0	0	$\dfrac{n_x + n_y}{2} -$
5	$n_x < \dfrac{n_{xy}^2}{n_y}$ $n_y < -\lvert n_{xy}\rvert$	0	0	$-\sqrt{\left(\dfrac{n_x - n_y}{2}\right)^2 + n_{xy}^2}$

$$n_x = n_\xi \cos^2\alpha + n_\eta \sin^2\alpha + 2\,n_{\xi\eta}\cos\alpha\sin\alpha \qquad (A2.3)$$

$$n_y = n_\xi \sin^2\alpha + n_\eta \cos^2\alpha - 2\,n_{\xi\eta}\cos\alpha\sin\alpha \qquad (A2.4)$$

$$n_{xy} = (n_\eta - n_\xi)\cos\alpha\sin\alpha + n_{\xi\eta}(\cos^2\alpha - \sin^2\alpha) \qquad (A2.5)$$

Now, the tension forces per unit length in the reinforcement (t_x, t_y) and the compression force in the concrete (c_c) can be calculated from the formulae given in Table A2.1.

The required amounts a_x and a_y of the reinforcement per unit length are calculated from

$$a_x = \frac{t_x}{f_{yd}} \qquad (A2.6)$$

$$a_y = \frac{t_y}{f_{yd}} \qquad (A2.7)$$

The design formulae are only valid if the reinforcement in both directions has the same design strength f_{yd}.

A compression failure of the concrete will only in very special cases of highly reinforced elements occur. The compressive stresses are given by:

$$\sigma_c = \frac{c_c}{h_e} \qquad (A2.8)$$

in which h_e is the thickness of the element. For bending design the element thickness might be approximated by

$$h_e = \frac{z_m}{3} \qquad (A2.9)$$

The compressive stresses should not exceed the concrete strength which may be taken as $0.8 \cdot f_{cd}$, taking into account the presence of irregular cracking.

Example A2.1 – Slab element

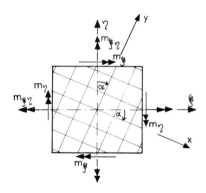

h $= 0.20$ m	$\gamma_c = 1.50$	$f_{ck} = 20$ MPa
d $= 0.17$ m	$\gamma_s = 1.15$	$f_{yk} = 500$ MPa
$z_m = 0.15$ m		

Structural analysis has been performed in a ξ-η-coordinate system which is inclined to the reinforcement directions x and y at an angle $\alpha = 22.5°$ and the following moments per unit length have been determined:

$$m_\xi = 15.9 \text{ kNm/m} \qquad m_\eta = 44.1 \text{ kNm/m} \qquad m_{\xi\eta} = 0 \text{ kNm/m}$$

The corresponding membrane forces in the tension zone are:

$$n_\xi = \frac{44.1}{0.15} = 294 \text{ kN/m}$$

$$n_\eta = \frac{15.9}{0.15} = 106 \text{ kN/m}$$

$$n_{\xi\eta} = 0$$

99

The acting membrane forces in the direction of the reinforcement are:

$$n_x = 294 \cdot 0.924^2 + 106 \cdot 0.383^2 + 0 = 266 \text{ kN/m}$$

$$n_y = 294 \cdot 0.383^2 + 106 \cdot 0.924^2 - 0 = 133 \text{ kN/m}$$

$$n_{xy} = (106 - 294) \cdot 0.924 \cdot 0.383 + 0 = -67 \text{ kN/m}$$

Since $\quad\quad\quad\quad n_x = 266 \text{ kN/m} > -|n_{xy}| = -67 \text{ kN/m}$

and $\quad\quad\quad\quad\quad n_y = 133 \text{ kN/m} > -|n_{xy}| = -67 \text{ kN/m}$

the formulae in line 1 of Table A2.1 must be applied.

$$t_x = 266 + 67 = 333 \text{ kN/m}$$

$$t_y = 133 + 67 = 200 \text{ kN/m}$$

$$c_c = -2 \cdot 67 = -134 \text{ kN/m}$$

$$f_{yd} = \frac{50}{1.15} = 43.5 \text{ kN/cm}^2$$

$$a_x = \frac{333}{43.5} = 7.7 \text{ cm}^2/\text{m}$$

$$a_y = \frac{200}{43.5} = 4.6 \text{ cm}^2/\text{m}$$

$$h_e = \frac{z_m}{3} = 0.05 \text{ m}$$

$$\sigma_c = \frac{0.134 \text{ MN/m}}{0.05 \text{ m}} = 2.7 \text{ MPa} < 0.8 \, f_{cd} = 0.8 \, \frac{20}{1.50} = 10.7 \text{ MPa}$$

Example A2.2 – Plate element with membrane forces

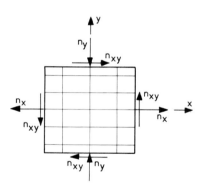

$h_e = 0.10 \text{ m}$ $\quad\quad\quad \gamma_c = 1.50$ $\quad\quad\quad f_{ck} = 20 \text{ MPa}$

$\quad\quad\quad\quad\quad\quad\quad\quad \gamma_s = 1.15$ $\quad\quad\quad f_{yk} = 500 \text{ MPa}$

The acting design membrane forces in the directions of the reinforcement have been determined as

$$n_x = 306 \text{ kN/m} \quad\quad\quad n_y = -136 \text{ kN/m} \quad\quad\quad n_{xy} = 128 \text{ kN/m}$$

Since $\quad\quad n_x = 306 \text{ kN/m} > \dfrac{n_{xy}^2}{n_y} = -120 \text{ kN/m} > -|n_{xy}| = -128 \text{ kN/m}$

and $\quad\quad\quad\quad n_y = -136 \text{ kN/m} < -|n_{xy}| = -128 \text{ kN/m}$

the formulae of line 3 of Table A2.1 must be applied.

$$t_x = 306 - \frac{128^2}{-136} = 426 \text{ kN/m}$$

$$t_y = 0$$

$$c_c = -136 + \frac{128^2}{-136} = -256 \text{ kN/m}$$

$$f_{yd} = \frac{50}{1.15} = 43.5 \text{ kN/cm}^2$$

$$a_x = \frac{425}{43.5} = 9.8 \text{ cm}^2/\text{m}$$

$$a_y = 0$$

The secondary reinforcement does not fulfil the requirements of §18.1.2.2.1 of the Model Code.

$$\sigma_c = \frac{0.256}{0.10} = 2.56 \text{ MPa} < 0.8 \, f_{cd} = 10.7 \text{ MPa}$$

A2.3 DESIGN PROCEDURE FOR ELEMENTS WITH SKEW REINFORCEMENT

Scope   The design procedure is applicable to plane reinforced concrete elements with skew reinforcement under any combination of membrane forces. It can also be applied to the tension zone of reinforced concrete slabs. In general, reinforcement must be provided in three different directions. If the force in one of the three directions is compressive, reinforcement in this direction can be omitted.

Use   If, in the most general case, a slab element is acted upon by moments m_ξ, m_η and $m_{\xi\eta}$ per unit length, the membrane forces acting in the tension or compression zone must be determined first using equations (A2.1). Then, the principal membrane forces n_1 and n_2 are calculated from:

$$n_1 = \frac{n_\xi + n_\eta}{2} + \sqrt{\left(\frac{n_\xi - n_\eta}{2}\right)^2 + n_{\xi\eta}^2} \tag{A2.10}$$

$$n_2 = \frac{n_\xi + n_\eta}{2} - \sqrt{\left(\frac{n_\xi - n_\eta}{2}\right)^2 + n_{\xi\eta}^2} \tag{A2.11}$$

The ratio between the principal membrane forces is called k.

$$k = \frac{n_2}{n_1} \tag{A2.12}$$

The acting membrane forces n_1 and n_2 are resisted by three internal forces t_x, t_y and t_z acting in the (x), (y) and (z) directions which form an angle of α, β and γ with the direction of n_1 (see Fig. A2.2). If the forces in one of these directions are compressive (negative), the corresponding reinforcement can be omitted and the force be carried by the concrete.

Figure A2.2   Directions of the reinforcement and of internal forces t_x, t_y, t_z

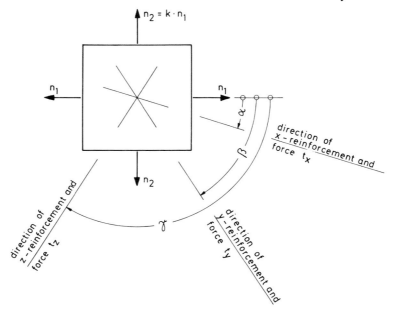

Table A2.2 Choice of angles β and γ for given direction $0 < \alpha < 90°$

Line	$k = n_2/n_1$	Number of reinforcement layers	Direction β of y-reinforcement	Direction γ of z-reinforcement or concrete force c_c	Forces in the reinforcement	Concrete force c_c in direction
1	$0 < k < 1$	3	$\alpha < \beta < \gamma_{oy}$	$\gamma_{oy} < \gamma < \gamma_{ox}$	t_x, t_y, t_z	–
2		3	$\gamma_{oy} < \beta < 180°$	$\gamma_{ox} < \gamma < \gamma_{oy}$	t_x, t_y, t_z	–
3		2	–	$\gamma = \gamma_{oy}$	t_x, t_z	–
4	$-\tan^2\alpha < k < 0$	2	$\alpha + 90° < \beta < \gamma_{oy}$	$\gamma = \dfrac{\alpha + \beta}{2}$	t_x, t_y	z
5		2	$\alpha + 90° < \beta < 180° - \alpha$	$\gamma = \dfrac{\alpha + \beta}{2}$	t_x, t_y	z
6		2	$\alpha + 90° < \beta < 180° - \alpha$ and $\beta > 2\gamma_{oy} - \alpha$	$\gamma = \dfrac{\alpha + \beta}{2}$	t_x, t_y	z
7	$k < -\tan^2\alpha$	1	–	$\gamma = \gamma_{oy}$	t_x	z

$\tan \gamma_{ox} = -k \cot \beta$ $\tan \gamma_{oy} = -k \cot \alpha$

The appropriate reinforcement directions can be chosen by use of Table A2.2. First the reinforcement direction with the smallest deviation from the n_1 direction is called (x). Its angle α should not exceed 45°. If the angle β of the reinforcement in the (y) direction is chosen according to lines 3 to 6 of Table A2.2, the forces in the (z) direction will be compressive so that reinforcement must only be provided in two directions.

The forces in the (x), (y) and (z) direction can be calculated from

$$t_x = \frac{n_1 \sin \beta \sin \gamma + n_2 \cos \beta \cos \gamma}{\sin (\beta - \alpha) \sin (\gamma - \alpha)} \tag{A2.13}$$

$$t_y = \frac{n_1 \sin \alpha \sin \gamma + n_2 \cos \alpha \cos \gamma}{\sin (\beta - \alpha) \sin (\beta - \gamma)} \tag{A2.14}$$

$$t_z = \frac{- n_1 \sin \alpha \sin \beta - n_2 \cos \alpha \cos \beta}{\sin (\beta - \gamma) \sin (\gamma - \alpha)} \tag{A2.15}$$

The calculation can be checked by

$$t_x + t_y + t_z = n_1 + n_2 \tag{A2.16}$$

The required amount of reinforcement per unit length in the (x), (y) and (z) direction is determined from

$$a_x = \frac{t_x}{f_{yd}} \tag{A2.17a}$$

$$a_y = \frac{t_y}{f_{yd}} \tag{A2.17b}$$

$$a_z = \frac{t_z}{f_{yd}} \quad \text{if } t_z > 0 \tag{A2.17c}$$

If t_z is a compressive force ($t_z < 0$) a check of the concrete compressive stresses can be performed using the relationship:

$$\sigma_c = \frac{t_z}{h_e} < 0.8 \, f_{cd} \tag{A2.18}$$

For slabs, the element thickness can be approximated by eq (A2.9).

Example A2.3 – Slab element

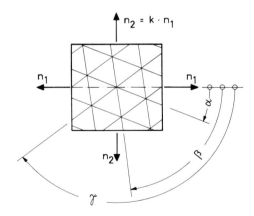

Slab element with same dimensions, materials and external loading as in Example A2.1:

$n_\xi = n_1 = 294 \text{ kN/m} \qquad n_\eta = n_2 = 106 \text{ kN/m}$
$k = 106/294 = 0.36$

Reinforcement is provided in three directions:

$\alpha = 22.5° \qquad \beta = 82.5° \qquad \gamma = 142.5°$

It must be checked that the requirements of Table A2.2, line 1, are fulfilled:

$\tan \gamma_{ox} = -k \cot \beta = -0.36 \cdot 0.13 = -0.047$
$\gamma_{ox} = 180 - 2.7 = 177.3°$

$$\tan \gamma_{oy} = -k \cot \alpha = -0.36 \cdot 2.41 = -0.869$$

$$\gamma_{oy} = 180 - 41 = 139°$$

$$\alpha = 22.5° < \beta = 82.5° < \gamma_{oy} = 139°$$

$$\gamma_{oy} = 139° < \gamma = 142.5° < \gamma_{ox} = 177.3°$$

$$t_x = \frac{n_1 \sin \beta \sin \gamma + n_2 \cos \beta \cos \gamma}{\sin (\beta - \alpha) \sin (\gamma - \alpha)} =$$

$$= \frac{294 \cdot 0.991 \cdot 0.609 + 106 \cdot 0.131 \cdot (-0.793)}{0.866 \cdot 0.866} = 222 \text{ kN/m}$$

$$t_y = \frac{n_1 \sin \alpha \sin \gamma + n_2 \cos \alpha \cos \gamma}{\sin (\beta - \alpha) \sin (\beta - \gamma)} =$$

$$= \frac{294 \cdot 0.383 \cdot 0.609 + 106 \cdot 0.924 \cdot (-0.793)}{0.866 \cdot (-0.866)} = 12 \text{ kN/m}$$

$$t_z = \frac{-n_1 \sin \alpha \sin \beta - n_2 \cos \alpha \cos \beta}{\sin (\beta - \gamma) \sin (\gamma - \alpha)} =$$

$$= \frac{-294 \cdot 0.383 \cdot 0.991 - 106 \cdot 0.924 \cdot 0.131}{(-0.866) \cdot 0.866} = 166 \text{ kN/m}$$

$$t_x + t_y + t_z = 222 + 12 + 166 = 400 \text{ kN/m} = n_1 + n_2$$

For reinforcement S500 ($f_{yd} = 50/1.15 = 43.5$ kN/cm²) the required amount of reinforcement per unit length is

$$a_x = \frac{222}{43.5} = 5.1 \text{ cm}^2/\text{m}$$

$$a_y = \frac{12}{43.5} = 0.3 \text{ cm}^2/\text{m}$$

$$a_z = \frac{166}{43.5} = 3.8 \text{ cm}^2/\text{m}$$

Example A2.4 – Slab element

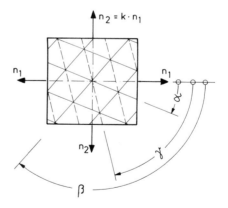

Dimensions, materials and external loadings are the same as in Examples A2.1 and A2.3.

$$n_\xi = n_1 = 294 \text{ kN/m} \qquad n_\eta = n_2 = 106 \text{ kN/m} \qquad k = 0.36$$

The requirements of line 4 of Table A2.2 can be fulfilled, therefore reinforcement in two directions only is possible:

$$\alpha = 22.5° \qquad \beta = 130°$$

$$\gamma_{oy} = 139° \text{ (see Example A2.3)}$$

$$\alpha + 90° = 112.5° < \beta = 130° < \gamma_{oy} = 139°$$

$$\gamma = \frac{\alpha + \beta}{2} = 76.3°$$

$$t_x = \frac{n_1 \sin \beta \sin \gamma + n_2 \cos \beta \cos \gamma}{\sin (\beta - \alpha) \sin (\gamma - \alpha)} =$$

$$= \frac{294 \cdot 0.766 \cdot 0.971 + 106 \cdot (-0.643) \cdot 0.238}{0.954 \cdot 0.806} = 263 \text{ kN/m}$$

$$t_y = \frac{n_1 \sin \alpha \sin \gamma + n_2 \cos \alpha \cos \gamma}{\sin (\beta - \alpha) \sin (\gamma - \alpha)} =$$

$$= \frac{294 \cdot 0.383 \cdot 0.971 + 106 \cdot 0.924 \cdot 0.238}{0.954 \cdot 0.806} = 172 \text{ kN/m}$$

$$t_z = \frac{-n_1 \sin \alpha \sin \beta - n_2 \cos \alpha \cos \beta}{\sin (\beta - \gamma) \sin (\gamma - \alpha)} =$$

$$= \frac{-294 \cdot 0.383 \cdot 0.766 - 106 \cdot 0.924 \cdot (-0.643)}{0.806 \cdot 0.806} = -36 \text{ kN/m}$$

$$t_x + t_y + t_z = 263 + 172 - 36 = 399 \cong n_1 + n_2$$

The required amount of reinforcement S500 ($f_{yd} = 43.5$ kN/cm^2) is

$$a_x = \frac{263}{43.5} = 6.0 \text{ cm}^2/\text{m}$$

$$a_y = \frac{172}{43.5} = 4.0 \text{ cm}^2/\text{m}$$

$$\sigma_c = \frac{0.036 \text{ NM/m}}{0.05 \text{ m}} = 0.72 \text{ MPa} < 0.8 \, f_{cd} = 10.7 \text{ MPa}$$

Example A2.5 – Plate element with membrane forces

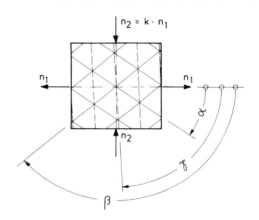

Plate element with same dimensions, materials and external forces as in Example A2.2.

$$n_1 = 340 \text{ kN/m} \qquad n_2 = -170 \text{ kN/m} \qquad k = -0.46$$

Reinforcement directions have been chosen to be

$$\alpha = 35° \qquad \beta = 140°$$

The requirements of line 5 of Table A2.2 are satisfied

$$-\tan^2 \alpha = -0.49 < k = -0.46 < 0$$
$$\alpha + 90° = 125° < \beta = 140° < 180° - \alpha = 145°$$
$$\gamma = \frac{\alpha + \beta}{2} = 87.5°$$

$$t_x = \frac{n_1 \sin \beta \sin \gamma + n_2 \cos \beta \cos \gamma}{\sin (\beta - \alpha) \sin (\gamma - \alpha)} =$$

$$= \frac{340 \cdot 0.643 \cdot 0.999 - 170 \cdot (-0.766) \cdot 0.044}{0.966 \cdot 0.793} = 293 \text{ kN/m}$$

$$t_y = \frac{n_1 \sin \alpha \sin \gamma + n_2 \cos \alpha \cos \gamma}{\sin (\beta - \alpha) \sin (\beta - \gamma)} =$$

$$= \frac{340 \cdot 0.574 \cdot 0.999 - 170 \cdot 0.819 \cdot 0.044}{0.966 \cdot 0.793} = 247 \text{ kN/m}$$

$$t_z = \frac{n_1 \sin \alpha \sin \beta - n_2 \cos \alpha \cos \beta}{\sin (\beta - \alpha) \sin (\gamma - \alpha)} =$$

$$= \frac{-340 \cdot 0.574 \cdot 0.643 + 170 \cdot 0.819 \cdot (-0.766)}{0.793 \cdot 0.793} = -369 \text{ kN/m}$$

$$t_x + t_y + t_z = 293 + 247 - 369 = 171 \cong n_1 + n_2 = 170 \text{ kN/m}$$

The required amount of reinforcement S500 ($f_{yd} = 43.5$ kN/cm^2) is:

$$a_x = \frac{293}{43.5} = 6.7 \text{ cm}^2/\text{m}$$

$$a_y = \frac{247}{43.5} = 5.7 \text{ cm}^2/\text{m}$$

$$\sigma_c = \frac{t_z}{h_e} = \frac{0.369}{0.05} = 7.5 \text{ MPa} < 0.8 \, f_{cd} = 10.7 \text{ MPa}$$

Appendix 3.
Limitation of concrete stresses at the serviceability limit state

A3.1 GENERAL

According to §15.4 of the Model Code, the compressive stresses in the concrete under rare combinations of actions during construction or in use should not exceed 60% of the characteristic value of concrete strength.

$$\sigma_{c,\,ser} \leqslant 0.6\,f_{ck} \qquad (A3.1)$$

This check is only required in those cases where high compressive stresses are foreseen (for example, in heavily reinforced sections of flexural members). Its purpose is to reduce the danger of excessive creep strains and/or of longitudinal cracking under the influence of transverse tensile stresses. The presence of transverse reinforcement can help in limiting the width of such cracks where they are liable to occur. If appropriate encircling tie reinforcement is provided, a check of the concrete stresses at the serviceability level may not be necessary (§6.2.2 of the Model Code, left side).

Since the verification is made at the serviceability level, the stress–strain relationships for concrete at the ultimate limit state (see 2.3.3 of this manual) cannot be used. For short time loading, equation (7.1) of the Model Code may be used as a stress–strain relationship for concrete. For simplification, a linear elastic calculation of the concrete stresses is possible, using the moduli of elasticity given in the Model Code for concrete (§2.5.2) and steel (§3.1.6.2). It must be noted that in this case the maximum concrete stresses will be overestimated.

It can be shown that in sections being designed correctly with respect to the ultimate limit state the concrete stresses may exceed $0.6\,f_{ck}$ at the serviceability level. This does not mean that there is any immediate danger of failure nor that the probability of reaching the ultimate limit state is increased.

A3.2 PROPOSALS FOR DESIGN AIDS FOR RECTANGULAR CROSS-SECTIONS

For practical convenience, the serviceability check of concrete stresses can be performed at the ultimate level by use of a global safety factor γ_f for actions:

$$1.35 \leqslant \gamma_f = \frac{S_d}{S_{ser}} \leqslant 1.50 \qquad (A3.2)$$

with:

S_d = design action-effect at the ultimate limit state

S_{ser} = action-effect at the serviceability limit state

For the design of rectangular cross-sections under *simple bending* it is possible to define the limit value of the reduced design bending moment

$$\mu_{Sd,\,lim} = \frac{M_{Sd,\,lim}}{bd^2\,f_{cd}} \qquad (A3.3)$$

This appendix is based on a proposal by G Mancini, Torino.

beyond which the design at the serviceability limit state will dominate:

$$\mu_{Sd, \, lim} = \beta_1 \, \gamma_f + \beta_2 \, f_{ck} + \beta_3 \qquad (A3.4)$$

with: $\qquad (A3.4$

γ_f = global safety factor for actions according to equation (A3.2)

f_{ck} = characteristic value of concrete compressive strength [MPa]

The coefficients β_1, β_2 and β_3 are given in Table A3.1 as a function of the reinforcement strength and the ratio of compression and tension reinforcement.

Table A3.1   Coefficients β_1, β_2 and β_3 for rectangular sections.

f_{yk}	ω_2/ω_1	β_1	β_2	β_3
220	0.0	0.371	0.0017	−0.270
	0.2	0.482	0.0043	−0.417
	0.4	0.735	0.0104	−0.813
	0.6	0.618	0.0259	−2.250
400	0.0	0.294	0.0021	−0.248
	0.2	0.482	0.0028	−0.512
	0.4	0 306	0.0029	−0.238
	0.6	0.271	0.0039	−0.183
500	0.0	0.065	0.0015	−0.069
	0.2	0.312	0.0023	−0.293
	0.4	0.159	0.0024	−0.063
	0.6	0.312	0.0033	−0.286

For the design of rectangular cross-sections under *prevailing compression* at the ultimate limit state, interaction diagrams are given in 3.3. Using a global safety factor γ_f as defined in equation (A3.2), equivalent interaction diagrams can be drawn for the serviceability check (see Fig. A3.1).

Due to the different combination of actions considered for the ultimate limit state and the serviceability limit state, we have generally

$$\frac{\mu_{Sd}}{\nu_{Sd}} \neq \frac{\mu_{ser}}{\nu_{ser}}$$

A correct method of verification of serviceability limit state consists of performing a double control on the interaction diagrams (Fig. A3.1) in the following way:

– entering the diagram related to the ultimate limit state with μ_{Sd} and ν_{Sd} gives the mechanical percentage of reinforcement ω;

– entering the diagram related to the serviceability limit state with μ_{ser} and ν_{ser} gives the mechanical percentage of reinforcement ω_{ser};

– the higher value between ω and ω_{ser} will then be chosen.

Figure A3.1   Interaction curves for a rectangular section with symmetrical reinforcement

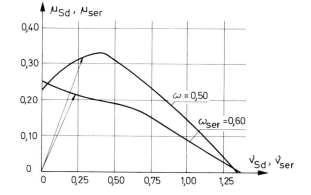

Example A3.1 –
Rectangular section

b = 0.25 m γ_s = 1.15 f_{yk} = 400 MPa
d = 0.45 m γ_c = 1.50 f_{ck} = 30 MPa

M_{Sd} = 280 kNm M_{ser} = 187 kNm

γ_f $= \dfrac{280}{187}$ = 1.50

f_{yd} $= \dfrac{400}{1.15}$ = 348 MPa f_{cd} $= \dfrac{30}{1.50}$ = 20 MPa

μ_{sd} $= \dfrac{280 \cdot 10^{-3}}{0.25 \cdot 0.45^2 \cdot 20}$ = 0.28

μ_{ser} $= \dfrac{187 \cdot 10^{-3}}{0.25 \cdot 0.45^2 \cdot 20}$ = 0.18

Using the General Table (Design Table 2) for the design at the ultimate limit state we get:

$$\omega_1 = 0.357; \qquad\qquad\qquad \omega_2 = 0$$

$$A_{s1} = \frac{0.357 \cdot 25 \cdot 45 \cdot 20}{348} = 23.1 \text{ cm}^2; \qquad A_{s2} = 0$$

For the design at the serviceability level we obtain from Table A3.1:

with $\omega_2/\omega_1 = 0$

$$\beta_1 = 0.294 \qquad \beta_2 = 0.0021 \qquad \beta_3 = -0.248$$

then, by mean of equation (A3.4)

$$\mu_{Sd,\,lim} = 0.26$$

and with $\omega_2/\omega_1 = 0.2$

$$\beta_1 = 0.482 \qquad \beta_2 = 0.0028 \qquad \beta_3 = -0.512$$

then

$$\mu_{Sd,\,lim} = 0.30$$

By a linear interpolation we can find the value $\omega_2/\omega_1 = 0.1$ which shows that the serviceability limit state is critical in the design and that the section must be reinforced with

$$A_{s1} = 23.1 \text{ cm}^2 \qquad \text{and} \qquad A_{s2} = 2.3 \text{ cm}^2$$

Example A3.2

Rectangular section with symmetric reinforcement:

b = 0.20 m γ_s = 0.15 f_{yk} = 400 MPa
d = 0.45 m γ_c = 1.50 f_{ck} = 25 MPa
μ_{Sd} = 0.320 μ_{ser} = 0.230
ν_{Sd} = 0.275 ν_{ser} = 0.204

From the ultimate limit state diagram, we find (Fig. A3.1):

$$\omega_1 = \omega_2 = 0.5$$

then $A_{s1} = A_{s2} = \dfrac{0.5 \cdot 20 \cdot 45 \cdot 16.67}{347.8} = 21.57 \text{ cm}^2$

From the serviceability limit state diagram, we find:

$$\omega_{1,\,ser} = \omega_{2,\,ser} = 0.6$$

then $A_{s1} = A_{s2} = \dfrac{0.6 \cdot 20 \cdot 45 \cdot 16.67}{347.8} = 25.88 \text{ cm}^3$

In the section design the serviceability limit state is critical.

Naturally, this procedure implies the necessity to supply a set of interaction diagrams, related to f_{ck}, f_{yk}, d_2/d, $\omega_{1,\,ser}$, $\omega_{2,\,ser}$. Such diagrams are not given in this manual.

Bibliography

1 CEB-Bulletin No 124/125: "Common unified Rules for different Types of Constructions and Material" (Vol I) and "CEB-FIP Model Code for Concrete Structures" (Vol II), Paris, 1978.
   (Bulletin 125 contains the basis for bending design in §10.)
2 CEB-Bulletin No 139: "Compléments au Code-Modèle CEB-FIP 1978", Paris, 1981.
   (Explains in §10 the basic assumptions and its application in short form.)
3 CEB-Bulletin No 36: H Rüsch, E Grasser, P S Rao, "Principes du calcul du béton armé sous des états de contraintes monoaxiaux", Paris, 1962.
   (Derivation of the bending theory, in particular of the parabolic—rectangular diagram.)
4 CEB-Bulletin No 75: E Grasser, A G Meseguer, P J Montoya, F Morán, "Manuel de Calcul CEB-FIP Flexion—Compression, 1ère partie", Paris, 1971.
   (First proposals for tables, diagrams and approximate formulae for the practical design of reinforced concrete sections.)
5 CEB-Bulletin No 76: J Perchat, "Manuel de Calcul CEB-FIP Flexion—Compression, 2ème partie", Paris, 1971.
   (Analytical treatment of the bending theory for the derivation of design aids.)
6 CEB-Bulletin No 82: "Manuel de Calcul CEB-FIP Flexion—Compression", Paris, 1972.
   (Proposes different aids (tables and diagrams) for the design of reinforced concrete sections, from which the design aids of this manual have been chosen. Contains also commented computer programs.)
7 CEB-Bulletin No 83: F Morán, "Documentation complémentaire au Manuel de Calcul CEB-FIP Flexion—Compression", Paris, 1973.
   (Contains studies on optimal design, e.g., minimum reinforcement area, optimal reinforcement distribution.)
8 CEB-Bulletin No 135: "Manuel de Calcul Flexion—Compression", Paris, 1980.
   (Final Draft of the Design Manual "Bending and Compression", presented to and approved by the 21st CEB-Plenary Session in Budapest, June 1980.)

This book is to be returned on or before
the last date stamped below.

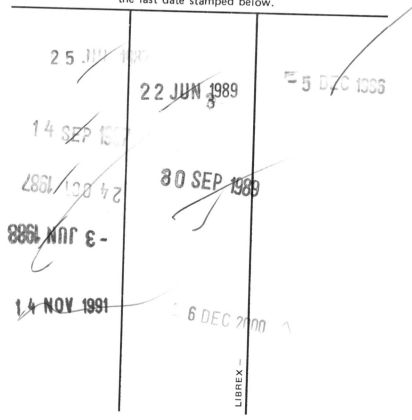